MBone: Interactive Multimedia on the Internet

Vinay Kumar

New Riders Publishing, Indianapolis, Indiana

MBone: Interactive Multimedia on the Internet

By Vinay Kumar

Published by:
New Riders Publishing
201 West 103rd Street
Indianapolis, IN 46290 USA

Printed in the United States of America 1 2 3 4 5 6 7 8 9 0

Kumar, Vinay, 1966-
MBone—interactive multimedia on the Internet / Vinay Kumar.
p. cm.
Includes index.
ISBN 1-56205-397-3
1. Interactive multimedia. 2. Internet (Computer network)
I..Title.
QA76.76.I59K85 1995
384.3'3—dc20 95-22592
CIP

Warning and Disclaimer

This book is designed to provide information about the MBone technology. Every effort has been made to make this book as complete and as accurate as possible, but no warranty or fitness is implied.

The information is provided on an "as is" basis. The author and New Riders Publishing shall have neither liability nor responsibility to any person or entity with respect to any loss or damages arising from the information contained in this book or from the use of the disks or programs that may accompany it.

Publisher Don Fowley
Marketing Manager Ray Robinson
Acquisitions Manager Jim LeValley
Managing Editor Tad Ringo

Product Development Specialist
Julie Fairweather
Acquisitions Editor
Jim LeValley
Production Editor
Sarah Kearns
Copy Editor
Amy Bezek
Technical Editor
Dino Farinacci
Assistant Marketing Manager
Tamara Apple
Acquisitions Coordinator
Tracey Turgeson
Publisher's Assistant
Karen Opal
Cover Designer
Karen Ruggles
Cover Illustrator
Jerry Blank
Book Designer
Sandra Schroeder
Manufacturing Coordinator
Paul Gilchrist
Production Manager
Kelly Dobbs
Production Team Supervisor
Laurie Casey
Graphics Image Specialists
Jason Hand, Clint Lahnen, Laura Robbins, Craig Small, Todd Wente
Production Analysts
Angela Bannan
Bobbi Satterfield
Production Team
Angela Calvert, Kim Cofer, George Hanlin, Erika Millen, Beth Rago, Erich J. Richter, Karen Walsh, Christine Tyner
Indexer
Bront Davis

About the Author

Vinay Kumar is the founder of a silicon valley startup company called MCast Communications Inc., which is based in Mountain View, California. At MCast, he leads the technological design and development of MBone-based products and services. Prior to founding MCast, Vinay had served as Senior Software Engineer at Enterprise Integration Technologies (EIT) since their founding days in early 1992. At EIT, he was the technology lead for several Internet-related projects with Stanford University, Focus:Hope, NTT (Japan), and IBM-NIIIP. Vinay was part of the team at EIT that founded CommerceNet—the first testbed for conducting electronic commerce over the Internet.

Vinay is also the sole author of freely available premier Internet software, such as Shared Mosaic (MBone), StoryBoard (MIME), Mmphone (MIME/MBone), and XShare. The Mmphone software was also proposed as an Internet standard at the last IETF meeting in Danvers, Massachusetts (April, 1995).

In addition, Vinay has published several papers for IEEE, Groupware, and World Wide Web conferences. He serves on the program review committee with Prof. Larry Rowe (U.C. Berkeley) and Prof. Brian Smith (Cornell) in organizing the SPIE Multimedia Internetworking Conference to be held in San Jose, California in 1996. Vinay has a B.S. in Computer Engineering from Indian Institute of Technology, and an M.S. in Computer Engineering from West Virginia University.

Trademark Acknowledgments

Dedication

To my Dad, Keshav, and Mom, Saroj, for their encouragement, faith, and support.

Acknowledgments

Although the author's name appears in the front of this book, the book actually has been a joint effort of several individuals. First and foremost is my family and friends who put up with my long and strange hours at the desk, especially Dad, Mom, Anita, Vikas, and Mary.

Jim LeValley and Don Fowley at New Riders are undoubtedly the best in the business to work with. Their understanding of the business, technology, and publishing is phenomenal. In addition, the attention to details that you find in this book is the result of some painstaking work done by the primary editors, Julie Fairweather and Sarah Kearns. The two kept the manuscript in line and helped me tremendously in not going astray with my thought processes. They have made this book extremely readable—excellent work indeed.

I could not have done the book in isolation. Numerous discussions on the Internet mailing lists and the IETF meetings provided me with answers to questions about the MBone. Several pieces of publicly available software provided by Steve Deering, Van Jacobson, Steve McCanne, Ron Frederick, Anders Klemets, Steve Casner, Lance Berc, Henning Schulzrinne, Ajit Thyagarajan, Eve Schooler, and Bill Fenner helped a lot in finding out about the inside details of the MBone. Thanks to Mark Weiser for sharing his bold comments and insights, helping me to clean up my thought processes. Berry Kercheval, James Blinkley, Angela Sasse, Shirley Wood should be thanked for helping review sections of the book for accuracy. Thanks to Laura Wilkes for sharing her research on news happenings in the Internet marketplace. Thanks also to Kenji Takahashi, Jeffrey Smith, and Atsuhiro Goto of Nippon Telephone and Telegraph Software Labs for letting me use their high-speed Internet connection and computers. Kevin Hughes should be thanked for his creative design of the book cover and training me on various aspects of graphics design. In addition, many thanks to Dino Farinacci for sparing time off his busy schedule to review the technical accuracy of the contents of the book.

Finally, it is the publishers and editors—Jim, Julie, Don, Sarah, David, and the rest of the team at New Riders—who helped create this product. They are simply the best, and have done an excellent job in getting this book out into the hands of the readers in such a short time. Hope you find the book informative and fun to read.

Contents at a Glance

Table of Contents

Foreword

"Any requests?" shouts the guitar player, Russ Haines, of the band Severe Tire Damage. The audience cries out, "Play 'Chris Killed Your Dog!'." A conventional rock music scene, except the band is surrounded by fiber-optic cable and high-powered workstations in the basement of Digital's Systems Research Center in Palo Alto, California, and the audience is replying from Japan, Finland, and Missouri, where they watch, listen, and respond instantly over the MBone.

In 1970, a few amazed pioneers exchanged files and e-mail over the early Internet. Their platform grew into the explosion of commerce, services, and information known as the World Wide Web. Today, in 1995, there are once again a few pioneers doing amazing things, and the platform is as revolutionary as the Web—it's called the MBone. If you want to know what will be exploding into homes, businesses, and lives in ten years, get to know the MBone today.

What makes a technology revolutionary? First, a revolutionary technology changes old ways by orders of magnitude. The digital computer does nothing different from the two-thousand-year-old abacus, but it does it a billion times faster. To do the same thing, much faster, offers a handle for starting a revolution. The "horseless carriage" and the "talking cylinder" were useful starting metaphors. The first printed books used type that appeared to have been hand scribed. The MBone is just the "multicast backbone"—it works just like the IP Internet, except it turns polynomial packet growth into no growth, creating huge new possibilities of bandwidth and interaction.

Second, a revolutionary technology must be a platform—that is, it must be the enabler, the door opener, for the unknown. Platforms raise people up, encourage their creativity, let them see further and strive for previously unimaginable goals. The MBone is an open platform, simple in concept, astounding in possibilities, and still so new that we know little of what it will finally enable.

Finally and fundamentally, a revolutionary technology must touch people. The telephone, the printing press, and the automobile all caused radical change because they reached deeply into the foundation of individual lives, where we construct ourselves from our interactions with others. The MBone erases time and space between people; hundreds, thousands, even millions of people can speak and see simultaneously all over the world. This will alter our social universe in ways no one can predict, except to say that the changes will be profound.

Until now, the MBone was mysterious. Only those already in the know could find their way around. At last, with this book, everyone can get to know and use the MBone. If a book like this had been written about the Internet in 1970, the World Wide Web might have happened 10 years sooner.

The author covers it all. For those who want to know just a little about the MBone revolution, the early chapters introduce basic concepts and possibilities. A chapter on system administration helps corporations join the MBone. Details of protocols and MBone applications will get programmers started. Specific hardware and software is reviewed by the brand name and contact person. And for those that are still not satisfied, the appendixes point to dozens of additional online sources of MBone information.

It has been fashionable in the past few years to speculate about how many TV channels we will have in a few years. Will it be 500? 5,000? The MBone, and its use by amateur bands like Severe Tire Damage, let us see the answer—five billion. One channel per person.

See you on the MBone.

Mark Weiser

Principal Scientist
Xerox Palo Alto Research Center (PARC)
Drummer, Severe Tire Damage
`http://www.ubiq.com/weiser`
`weiser@ubiq.com`

September, 1995

introduction

Computer technology takes a major upswing almost every three to five years. It jumps up a few notches, and every such notch starts a new generation of technology and related products and services. In the last five years, the two most popular and powerful technologies that have come into being are the *World Wide Web* (WWW) and the MBone. The Web is a simple client/server technology much like the traditional database technologies (Sybase, Oracle), except it works over the wide-area Internet and has a graphical user interface. The MBone, on the other hand, is a bigger and better-quality invention from a technological point of view. It upgrades the computing and networking infrastructure at the operating system and network routing level, while still being backward compatible in some sense. The MBone software tools are not tied to a specific form of computing—that is, client/server or peer-to-peer; it can be adapted to do either.

I personally have been involved with both technologies since their early days as a user, designer, and developer of new software tools in these exciting domains. In my experience, the MBone has the potential to deliver what interactive TV was supposed to years ago. The MBone also has the potential to create truly interactive community networking applications, where "community" means a large number of desktop computers connected to the Net. Nothing scales like the MBone when it comes to real-time delivery of content to a large number of sites without creating large bottlenecks at the CPU or the network. That is why the MBone is a more exciting domain to a large community of users today. How and why this technology affects us as users of computer-based communication is what prompted me to write this book.

The MBone has been used worldwide for over three years as a very successful testbed for real-time interactive multimedia. Experiments conducted by universities, research organizations, and corporations in delivering time-critical multimedia information content simultaneously to a large number of sites over the MBone have been very successful. The underlying MBone technology—called *IP multicasting*—has wide support and commitment from almost all operating system vendors, including Microsoft and Apple, as well as router vendors such as Cisco Systems, 3COM Corp., and others. The MBone is now provided as a service—on top of your IP service—by most IP service providers. Thus, the MBone technology is not only an Internet standard, but also widely deployed and commercially supported. The commercialization of the MBone is happening at an aggressive pace at various levels. The operating systems, Internet routers, Internet services, and a new class of MBone applications are all being gradually introduced into the market by computer hardware and software manufacturers. Some of these developments in the marketplace have been covered in this book.

The reason some of us have not experienced the MBone is because most of the freely available MBone applications exist only for the Unix and X Windows computing platforms and are not commercially supported. Although commercial outfits are just now beginning to appear, pledging to provide and support such networking applications, these are highlighted in the book as well. Another reason why some of us have not yet experienced the MBone is because we don't know where to start. Using the MBone tools is easy; in fact, after the installation and the configuration phase, it is easier than using Mosaic or Netscape. Unfortunately, installation and configuration of the MBone is still not as easy as we would like it to be, but it is getting better and better with every major release of operating system kernels and software multicast routers.

This book hopefully will make the life of system and network administrators much easier. One of the goals behind writing this book was to address some of the MBone issues facing *Internet service providers* (ISPs) today. The MBone potentially could change how ISPs manage the Internet packet traffic through their network and, in turn, manage bandwidth for a fair price. The success of the MBone is quite closely tied to ISPs supporting this technology. Most ISPs have been very enthusiastic about using, developing, and supporting the MBone. For all of those ISPs who have not joined the MBone movement yet, I hope that this book will get them committed to providing the MBone as a service to their customers. I am quite convinced that proper application of this technology will not only bring IP service providers larger revenues, but also will help manage their network bandwidth use.

This book also focuses on details about the underlying MBone technology—that is, the IP multicasting scheme. The new parameters that influence IP multicasting, and how multicasting works in practice between desktop applications, the desktop operating system, and IP routers, are also discussed in this book. In my opinion, this is important for most MIS managers because they will be able to make important decisions about how best to deploy and use this technology and various associated tools and services within their organizations. Training to use the MBone tools within an organization or, optimally, between remote organizations, is very important. This book takes a brief look at how to conceptually view these tools and use them most productively.

Because MBone support by the vendors is still in the consolidation phase, a lot of the relevant information and, therefore, the software, is still only available online via the Internet. This book details various FTP and Web sites that provide such resources. We all know that a lot of hardware and software from the computer industry are constantly being revised and upgraded. During the short course of writing this book, several pieces of MBone software have already undergone three revisions. Most users are always trying to catch up to the most current version number; this is why I decided to leave one of the chapters simply as an URL to a Web site, which will maintain the most up-to-date and current information about commercial MBone software and hardware resources. You have to thank the publishers of this book for being open to such a neat and novel concept in publishing. I sincerely hope that you find the book informative and interesting—it certainly was for me.

Vinay Kumar

New Riders Publishing

The staff of New Riders Publishing is committed to bringing you the very best in computer reference material. Each New Riders book is the result of months of work by authors and staff who research and refine the information contained within its covers.

As part of this commitment to you, the NRP reader, New Riders invites your input. Please let us know if you enjoy this book, if you have trouble with the information and examples presented, or if you have a suggestion for the next edition.

Please note, though: New Riders staff cannot serve as a technical resource for the MBone or for related questions about software- or hardware-related problems.

If you have a question or comment about any New Riders book, there are several ways to contact New Riders Publishing. We will respond to as many readers as we can. Your name, address, or phone number will never become part of a mailing list or be used for any purpose other than to help us continue to bring you the best books possible. You can write us at the following address:

New Riders Publishing
Attn: Publisher
201 W. 103rd Street
Indianapolis, IN 46290

If you prefer, you can fax New Riders Publishing at (317) 581-4670.

You can send electronic mail to New Riders at the following Internet address:

jfairweather@newriders.mcp.com

NRP is an imprint of Macmillan Computer Publishing. To obtain a catalog or information, or to purchase any Macmillan Computer Publishing book, call (800) 428-5331.

Thank you for selecting *MBone: Interactive Multimedia on the Internet*!

part I

The MBone Architecture

chapter 1

The Internetwork Primer

One of the most widely successful and robust pieces of Internet technology existing today is the *Virtual Multicast Backbone On the interNEt*, otherwise known as the MBone. This technology forms the backbone of the Internet for distributing real-time multimedia information to millions of computer desktops worldwide. Computer networks today are more important than ever—and with the arrival of fast multimedia desktop computers, coupled with computer networks, some users believe that the "cable-ization" (as in cable TV) of the computer networks and the computer itself is not too far away. The possibilities of making multimedia information available over computer networks as soon as it gets created on one or more computer desktops has now become feasible.

This book uniquely describes the importance of this technology in enabling new ways of communicating between Internet hosts. You will get a glimpse of how the MBone relates to the TCP/IP protocol suite at the lower infrastructure layers, and to the groupware marketplace at the application or the desktop layer. Potential scenarios and relationships between the cable TV industry and the MBone multimedia delivery systems are also investigated here.

The internal details and operation of the MBone technology, along with the associated standardization efforts that are underway, are highlighted in this book. Industry support for this technology is also discussed. In addition, various logistical issues relating to the installation, use, and administering of the MBone within an organization are covered in great detail.

Understanding Local Area Networks

A computer *network* is a communication system that connects a set of computing subsystems together. The computing subsystems, also called *hosts*, could be a single user computer such as a DOS or Windows machine, a multiuser Unix workstation, or a network printer. Computer networks enable communication between such subsystems.

A *local area network* (LAN) interconnects a set of hosts within a certain close vicinity, such as within a building or a floor. The most popular LAN technologies are Ethernet and Token Ring. A LAN typically operates at speeds higher than a traditional fax-modem—Ethernet operates at 10 Mbps (million bits per second), whereas IBM's Token Ring operates at 4 and 16 Mbps. Newer LAN technologies such as *Fiber Distributed Data Interface* (FDDI) and *Copper Distributed Data Interface* (CDDI) have also begun to appear in LAN environments. FDDI operates ten times faster than Ethernet—that is, at 100 Mbps.

Connecting to a LAN

Each host on a computer network has a network interface that enables the computer to connect to the network. The network interface is achieved with a hardware/software card that is placed inside each host computer. Therefore, in the case of an Ethernet network, the network interface card is the Ethernet card. Similarly, one will need an FDDI network interface card to get connected to an FDDI LAN network.

Communicating with Other LANs

The computers on one computer network can communicate with other distinct networks through *gateways* or *routers*. As the name suggests, routers not only move information from one computer on one network to another computer on another network, but also decide what route the information should take to get to the destination host. Thus, these routers form the communication backbone of computer networks. Such communication and linking between various distinct networks constitute what is called the *Internetwork* (see fig. 1.1). Thus, Internetworking facilitates the flow of information from one network to another.

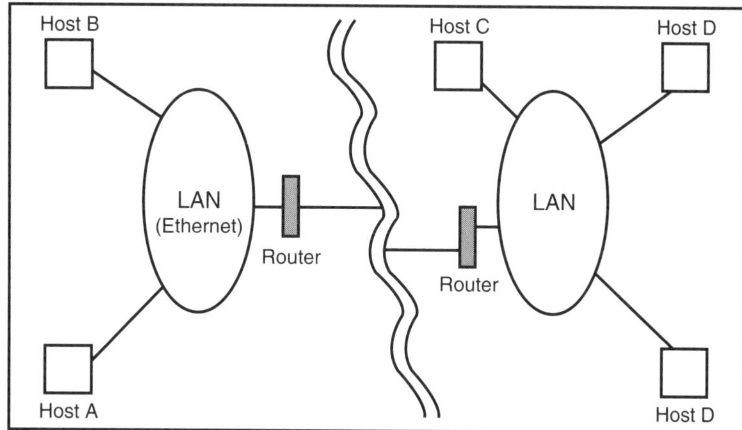

Figure 1.1

An Internetwork created by joining two distinct LANs.

The *Internet Protocol* (IP) is the primary Internetworking protocol used to connect computer networks worldwide. It is the protocol used by the Internet, which connects data networks in more than 50 countries and all seven continents. The IP protocol has been the most successful interconnecting protocol—the Internet has grown from a few hundred networks in the 1980s to more than 10,000 interconnected networks today.

The Evolution of the Internet

During the early 1970s, the U.S. military, under its *Defense Advanced Research Projects Agency* (DARPA—now called ARPA), established funding for ARPANet, which connected several U.S. universities and research organizations. The Internet came into being around 1980—DARPA started converting the machines connected to its research network to use the new TCP/IP protocols. The transition became complete in January 1983, when DARPA demanded that all computers connected to ARPANet use TCP/IP [7] (see bibliography).

The Internet now has grown into an international computer network that links millions of computers used by universities, research organizations, corporations, and individuals worldwide. The Internet is built on what is called the *Transmission Control Protocol/Internet Protocol* (TCP/IP) protocol stack [Reynolds, RFC 901]—TCP/IP is the universal protocol of the Internet. This protocol enables universal addressing of all the hosts on the Internet. The protocol stack is shown in figure 1.2.

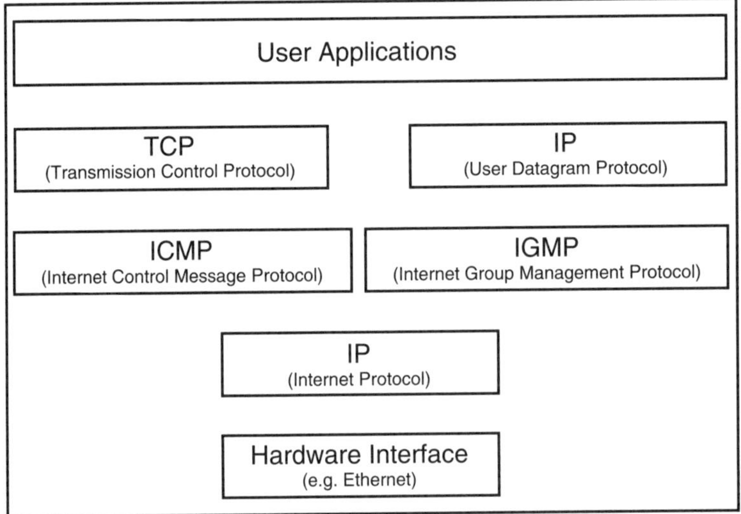

Figure 1.2

The TCP/IP protocol stack, showing the layered model.

Internet Packet Switching

Information flows over the Internet in the form of a *datagram* or *packet*. These packets are routed from the source to the destination through a switching mechanism referred to as *packet switching*. Packet switching works much like the *Post Office Protocol* (POP) in that information is enveloped in a packet and stamped with the destination address. This addressed packet then gets routed to the destination without any virtual circuit being established between the original source and final destination—just like a voice telephone call. The route the packet takes on packet networks like the Internet might not be the same each time between the same source and destination—it is dynamic in nature. Refer to the cited source by Tenenbaum for more details [1].

There are three kinds of switching mechanisms—circuit switching, packet switching, and message switching. The Internet utilizes the packet switching mechanism.

Understanding Internet Address Classes

Figure 1.3 illustrates a sample packet. The header portion of a packet contains the routing information, such as the sender and receiver host's network address.

Header	User Information/Data

Figure 1.3

User information encapsulated inside a packet.

Internet addresses are 32 bits long.

Conceptually, each Internet address is a pair consisting of the net id and the host id. The net id identifies a network, and the host id identifies a host on that network. Based on these two parts, IP addresses are classified into five classes: A, B, C, D, and E (see fig. 1.4). It is the first byte or the first decimal number that decides the class of an Internet address. Thus, class D addresses range from 224.0.0.0 to 239.255.255.255. Class D addresses, which are reserved for the MBone, are also called *multicast* or *group* addresses.

Class E addresses are currently not defined or implemented on the Internet.

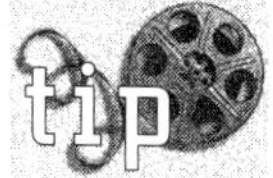

Details on Internet addressing can be found in Reynolds and Postel [RFC 990 and 997].

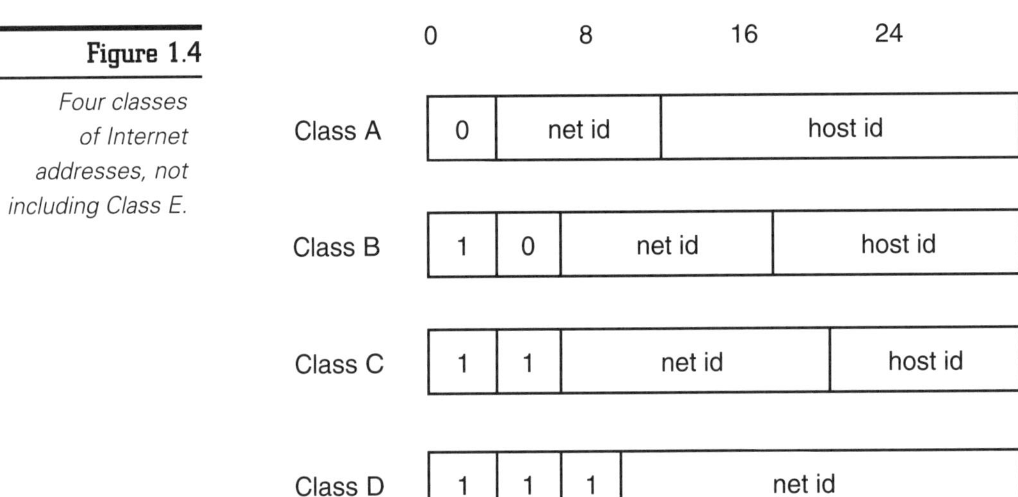

Figure 1.4

Four classes of Internet addresses, not including Class E.

The Internet Engineering Task Force

The *Internet Engineering Task Force* (IETF) is the protocol engineering and development arm of the Internet. The IETF is a large, open, international community of network designers, operators, vendors, and researchers concerned with the evolution of the Internet architecture and the smooth operation of the Internet. It is open to any interested individual.

The IETF holds meetings three times per year. The actual technical work of the IETF is done in its *working groups*, which are organized by topic into several areas (e.g., routing, network management, security, and so on). Each working group is a small, focused effort between individuals worldwide, with the underlying principle being rough consensus and running pieces of developed software and hardware. The working groups meet at the IETF meetings, but do not make any decisions at these meetings. The real work is done through e-mail communication over the Internet.

Managing the IETF

The internal management of the IETF is handled by the area directors. Together with the chairperson of the IETF, they form the *Internet Engineering Steering Group* (IESG). The operational management of the Internet standards process is handled by the IESG under the auspices of the Internet Society. Another body of the Internet Society, the *Internet Architecture Board* (IAB), is responsible for overall architectural considerations on the Internet. It also serves to adjudicate disputes on the standards process.

Publishing Internet Documents and Standards

Proposals for Internet standards can be found in two types of documents: *Internet Drafts* (IDs) and *Request for Comments* (RFCs). Internet Drafts have absolutely no formal status and can be changed or deleted at any time. The Secretariat maintains an Internet Drafts index. RFCs are the official document series of the IAB, and are archived permanently—that is, they are never deleted; once an RFC is published, it will never change. Most of these documents can be easily found online or in the form of IETF proceedings. See Appendix A, "MBone Resources on the Internet," to find out how to access RFCs.

It is important to note that not all RFCs are Internet standards.

Multimedia on the Internet

Multimedia is a combination of one or more media that might include text, graphics, animation, voice, and video. Voice and video media can be digital or analog. In normal circumstances, the human voice is analog, as are television/VCR video signals. Analog audio and video signals are continuous in nature—they convey meaning only when presented continuously in time. A timing relationship must be maintained to synchronize a presentation, as when human lip movements correspond to speech. Such media types requiring timing relationships and synchronization are also referred to as *isochronous* media.

Converting Analog to Digital Signals

An understanding of how analog signals work is essential to understanding digital signals. A digital version of real-world audio and video signals is obtained by feeding the analog signal into an *Analog-to-Digital Converter* (ADC), as shown in figure 1.5. The output of such a digitizer is a digital audio/video signal.

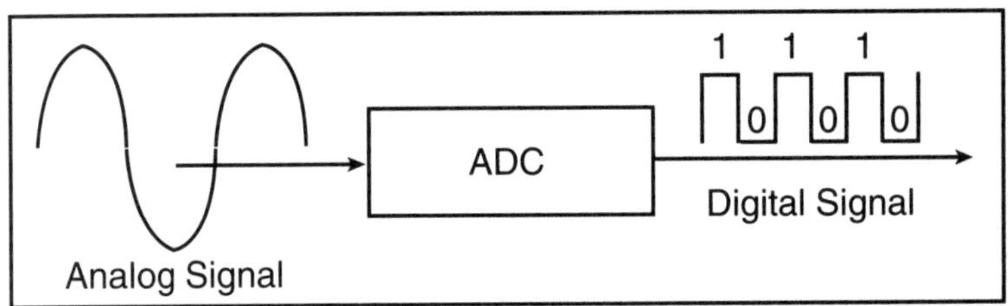

Figure 1.5

An ADC showing analog to digital conversion.

Not all digital audio or video is equal to, or necessarily better than, its analog counterpart. The ultimate digital sound or video quality depends on sample rates and resolution. The faster the sample rates and the more bits used to determine the value of the samples, the better the quality. Table 1.1 specifies some numbers for uncompressed multimedia data requirements.

Table 1.1

Specifications for Uncompressed Multimedia Data

Media Type	Specifications	Data Rate (Per Second)
Voice quality audio	1 channel, 8-bit samples at 8 KHz	64 Kbps
MPEG encoded audio	Equivalent to CD quality	384 Kbps
CD quality audio	2 channels, 16-bit samples at 44.1 KHz	1.4 Mbps
MPEG-2 encoded audio	640×480 pixels/frame, 24 bits/pixel	.42 Mbps
NTSC quality video	640×480 pixels/frame, 24 bits/pixel	27 Mbps
HDTV quality video	1280×720 pixels/frame, 24 bits/pixel	81 Mbps

Multimedia Conferencing

Interest in the transmission and reception of continuous media over computer networks has been around since the early days of ARPANet. This transmission and reception of multimedia data streaming simultaneously between various hosts is also called *conferencing*. According to [9], continuous voice-based conferencing was initially conducted in 1976. The first Internet packet voice protocol, which indicates a standard for sending voice over the Internet, was specified formally in 1977 [10]; a packet video standard followed in 1981 [11]. Recently, interest in such multimedia conferencing has increased; several desktop machines (SUN, SGI, DEC, HP, PowerPC, and WindowsPC) now support vast multiple capabilities. These machines come bundled with audio, video hardware, and limited software. More and more of these machines are also getting connected to high-speed networks like the Internet. As a result, more and more users are beginning to share multimedia information, using the model shown in figure 1.6.

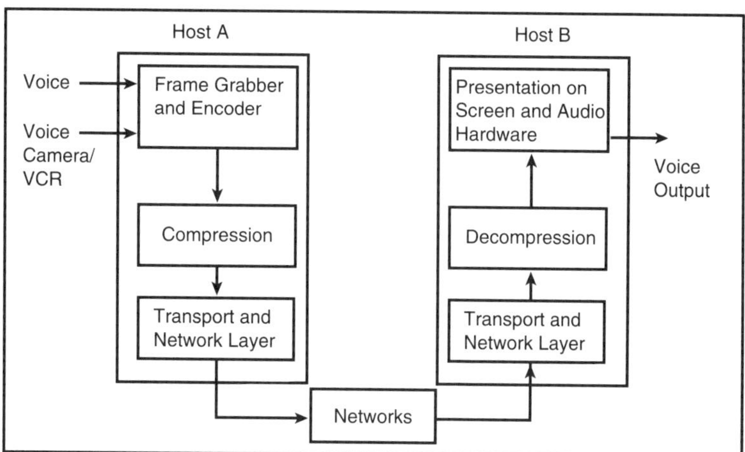

Figure 1.6

The system components for audio and video network transmission.

Multimedia Distribution Architecture

Figure 1.6 portrays how continuous media like a video signal enters the system at Host A and gets delivered to Host B over computer networks in almost real-time. The same model can then be extended to voice signals as well. A video camera/VCR (such as a Sony TR-61 palmcorder) provides the continuous video feed. This analog video information is fed directly into a Frame Grabber and Encoder hardware such as a VideoBlaster card on PCs, or a SunVideo card on a Sun machine. These video hardware boards digitize the analog video signal into digital data, followed by encoding. *Encoding* is how fast the analog incoming data is sampled; potential encoding schemes include the *National Television Standards Committee* (NTSC), *Phase Alteration Line* (PAL), *High Definition Television* (HDTV), and so on.

Because this digital data is generated in very large quantities, it thus needs to be compressed for more efficient transport to Host B over the network. Compression is done either in hardware or software, and some of the video compression techniques include the *Joint Photographic Experts Group* (JPEG), *Motion Pictures Experts Group* (MPEG), *NetVideo* (NV), H.261, and so on. The compressed video data is now transmitted by Host A to Host B.

At Host B, a reverse process helps to render the video signal in its digital form on the screen (see fig. 1.6). The speed with which a video signal can be rendered on Host B after it is generated on Host A depends on the following:

- Speed (CPU and operating system) of each host involved
- Speed of video encoding and decoding hardware
- Speed of compression and decompression
- Speed of the network to which each host is connected

The video data received at Host A can also be seen on a TV monitor in analog form, depending on what the video hardware and software allows.

Mixing Multimedia at the Network Level

From the example in the previous section, it is interesting to note that the same computer network can now be used for multiplexing and demultiplexing different kinds of media streams—such as text, graphics, audio, and video—simultaneously for multiple hosts. Figure 1.7 will help explain this concept of multiplexing and demultiplexing further.

Figure 1.7

The multiplexing and demultiplexing of multimedia information on computer networks.

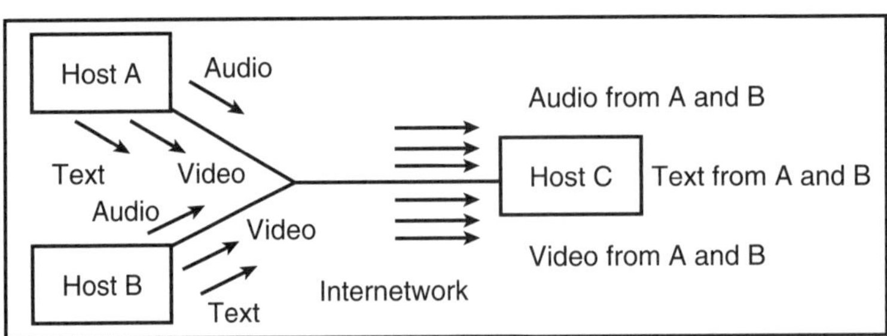

As shown in figure 1.7, multiple hosts can send and receive various kinds of multimedia information simultaneously over a computer internetwork. It is the receiver's job (Host C in this example) to demultiplex the network media streams. Demultiplexing might require determining who is sending what media stream, how to render each media and with what priority, and so on.

Introducing the MBone

As mentioned earlier, MBone stands for the *Virtual Multicast Backbone On the interNEt*. The *MBone* is a technology that enables distribution of and access to real-time interactive multimedia on the Internet. Distributing such isochronous media in a large-scale manner over packet networks such as the Internet was not feasible before the MBone was invented and deployed.

Isochronous media refers to a class of multimedia data that requires delivery from source to destination within a certain bounded time. As noted earlier, typical examples of such a media types are real-time voice and video. The MBone enables delivery of such media on the Internet. Network scalability of such technologies is very important, especially when large-scale community use of resources are involved. The next section describes network scalability in more detail.

Defining Network Scalability

What does network scalability mean? *Network scalability* is essentially a solution to specific problems or limitations in communications. Any traditional multiparty communication system between multiple hosts on the Internet involves the following steps:

1. First, each information packet at the transmitting source host is replicated into the same number of copies as the number of destination receiving hosts.
2. Next, one copy of the information packet is forwarded to each destination.
3. Finally, the destination hosts receive, assemble, and process these packets of information from each sender.

This model, however, puts heavy limitation on the number of destinations that could be involved in such a multiparty communication—the network traffic (in transporting each copy to the destination) and source host computations (in making copies of each information packet) increase linearly with the number of destination hosts. Any technology that helps to overcome the previously mentioned limitations is considered a network scalable solution. Figure 1.8 shows some of these aspects of the traditional model.

As shown in figure 1.8, link L-1 and Host Z are heavily loaded. Links L-2 through L-5, however, have moderate network traffic on them. The MBone, on the other hand, has overcome such limitations—there is no replication of packets by each host involved in a multiparty communication. If the same group of hosts were communicating over the MBone, then the network traffic and host CPU utilization will appear similar to that shown in figure 1.9.

Figure 1.8

A typical multiparty communication system.

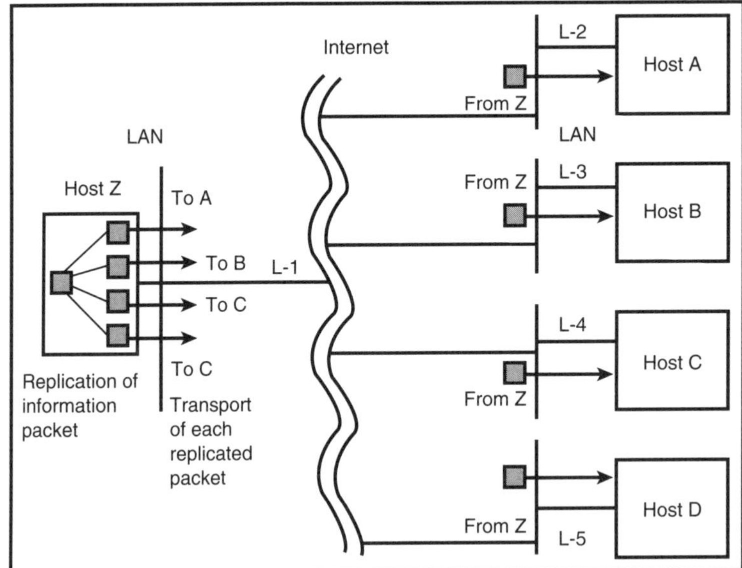

Figure 1.9

A group of Internet hosts communicating over the MBone.

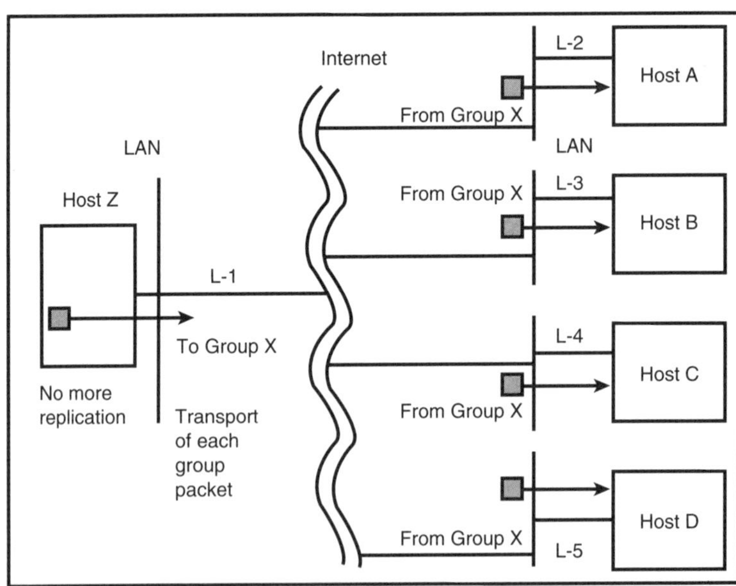

Host A no longer replicates information packets for each intended receiver, and the network traffic over link L-1 remains much lower and the same, irrespective of the number of intended recipients. This is a major improvement over the traditional model for multiparty communications. You might have noted, however, that the sender (Host A) no longer sends each packet to the address of a specific individual. The addressing has been replaced by what is called the *group address*. A group address is also called the *multicast address*, which was defined earlier to be the class D Internet address.

The MBone itself consists of a subset of Internet routers that understand the Internet class D addressed packets and their routing. Such MBone routers have been deployed in the core Internet communication infrastructure. In addition, the ability to create and understand class D addressed Internet packets is now available in most industry-shipped desktop computers, which include Unix workstations, Windows PCs, and Macintosh machines.

The Growth of the MBone

The multicast address concept for group communication was invented by Steve Deering in his Ph.D thesis at Stanford University, and later developed at Xerox PARC. Van Jacobson and his group at *Lawrence Berkeley Labs* (LBL), as well as Steve Casner at the *Information Science Institute* (ISI) and several other engineers, helped enhance the MBone design and deployment. The MBone was first deployed in the first few Internet routers in 1992, and has since experienced phenomenal growth, bypassing all expectations—currently, about 1,700 of the Internet routers are on the MBone. This figure, however, does not include the number of machines or hosts that join and use the MBone on a regular basis. As of this writing, the MBone is already deployed and used in all the continents. Figure 1.10 shows the growth of the MBone in terms of the number of Internet routers that have been upgraded to join the MBone.

IP multicast is the class D addressing scheme in IP. IP multicasting for the Internet was first adopted at the *Internet Engineering Task Force* (IETF) meeting in March 1992, and acquired the name "MBone" after the July 1992 IETF meeting. Initially, the MBone backbone was termed "virtual," because the MBone capabilities (class D addressing and/or routing) did not exist in production-level Internet routers and desktop operating systems. Only a subset of IP routers knew how to route multicast packets. The situation has changed considerably, however—several production-level multicast routers are now available in the market, and almost all operating systems come bundled with multicast support. The MBone, therefore, has been transformed from a virtual backbone to a semi-real one, and is on its way to becoming a fully deployed, permanent, real backbone.

Figure 1.10

The growth curve of the MBone.

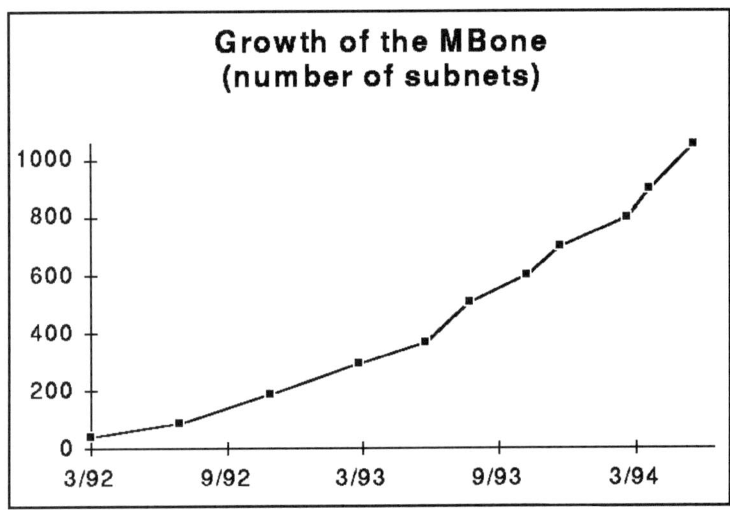

The later sections in this chapter describe the exact nature and relationship between IP multicasting and the MBone.

IP Multicasting and the MBone

The class D Internet addresses (first byte value between 224 and 239) are used for Internet-wide IP multicasting. A small subset of this class D address space has been set aside for multimedia conferencing over the Internet—it is this subset of class D addresses that constitute the MBone. The address space assigned by *Internet Address Number Authority* (IANA) for use by the MBone includes the range 224.2.*.*.

Now that you have a background on Internet multicast addressing, which facilitates multiparty communications on the Internet, you will now examine how multiparty communications compares to traditional unicast-based, point-to-point communications. As mentioned earlier, in traditional or IP unicast-based communication, there is more network and CPU overhead at each site if multiple sites are involved in communication simultaneously. The IP unicast architecture does not scale very well for time-critical, multihost, simultaneous communication.

As shown in figure 1.11, in the case of IP multicast routing, the routing and replication of packets is handled by the modified Internet routers mr-2, mr-3, and mr-4—not by individual Internet hosts. Also, note that the presence of an unmodified Internet router, r-1, does not affect the multicast behavior. An unmodified Internet router such as r-1 sees the class D addressed multicast packet as a standard IP packet, and therefore routes the packet appropriately.

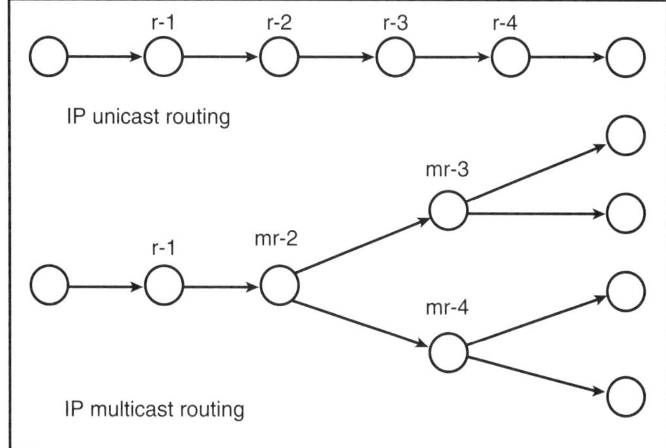

Figure 1.11

The difference between unicast and multicast routing.

The Role of Mrouters

IP multicast routers, referred to as *mrouters*, take the responsibility of distributing and replicating the multicast data stream to their destinations. The MBone topology of mrouters is designed in such a manner that it facilitates efficient distribution of packets without congesting any node or network link inappropriately. In this way, IP multicast-based routing facilitates distributed hosts to achieve time-critical, real-time communications over wide area IP networks.

Distributing IP Multicast Packets

IP multicasting, as the name suggests, enables distribution of IP packets to one or more Internet sites; it does not imply a general broadcast to all the Internet hosts. The multicast packets are class D addressed packets, which are also called *group addressed* packets.

Multicast addresses are not physical Internet addresses that are tied to a specific physical network interface at a certain physical site. These are logical group addresses that are dynamic in nature—that is, they exist as long as there is a group of Internet sites interested in sending and receiving multicast data.

A site can express an interest in becoming a member of a certain multicast group (224.2.4.4, for example) by sending an *Internet Group Management Protocol* (IGMP) join message. The site can now send and receive information addressed to this group. Only the sites that have expressed an interest in this multicast address group will receive information addressed to 224.2.4.4. You do not have to be a member of this group, however, to transmit packets or information to this group. The routing of such multicast packets is done through the *Distance Vector Multicasting Routing Protocol* (DVMRP), which is an Internet standard [RFC 1075]. Besides DVMRP, another scheme originally developed by John Moy, called *Multicast Open Shortest Path Factor* (MOSPF), is also being investigated as a complementary multicast routing scheme.

The MBone Tree and Mesh Topology

The MBone topology on the Internet is a tree and a mesh. The tree topology can be seen in figure 1.12 near the leaf nodes. The connections between mrouters of major Internet service provider nodes constitute the mesh topology.

It is anticipated that within a continent, the MBone topology will be a combination of mesh and star—the backbone and regional (or mid-level) networks will be linked by a mesh of tunnels among mrouted machines located primarily at interconnection points of the backbones and regionals. Between continents, there will probably be only one or two tunnels, preferably terminating at the closest point on the MBone mesh. In the U.S., this may be on the Ethernets at the two *Federal Internet eXchanges* (FIXes) in California and Maryland. Tunnels are described in more detail later in this chapter.

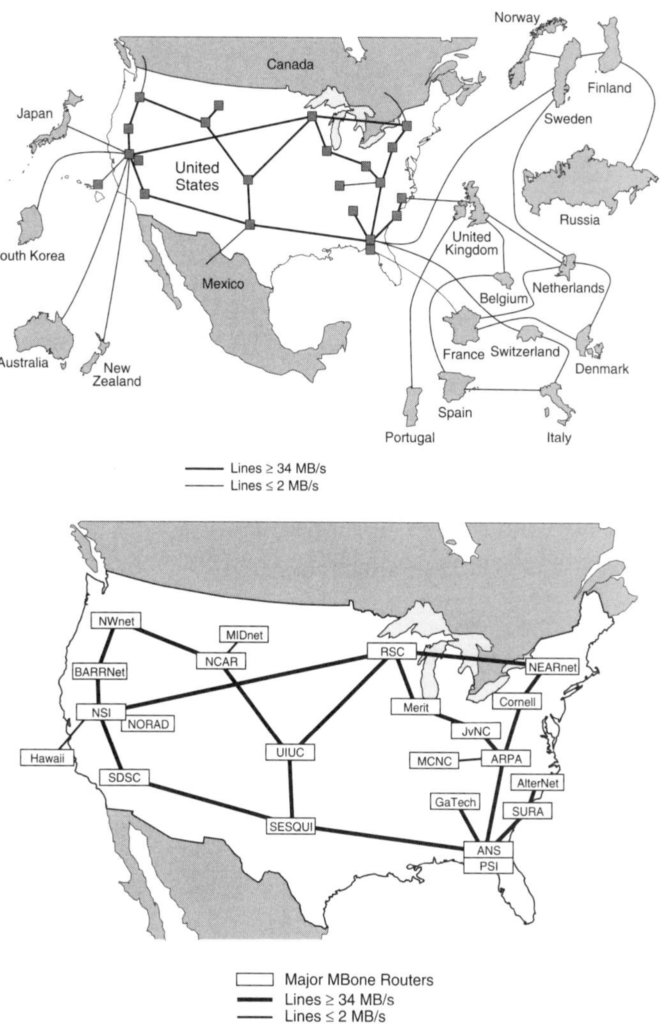

Figure 1.12

The topology of the MBone.

Time To Live (TTL)

Each multicast address has a *Time To Live* (TTL) value associated with it. TTL facilitates managed distribution of multicast data traffic over the MBone. It enables users or applications to specify how far the multicast traffic should go on the Internet—that is, how many IP router hops are required to get to the destination.

TTL acts as a scoping mechanism for inter-domain routing of multicast packets. Each multicast router on the MBone uses a threshold value associated with it to truncate multicast traffic to the leaf routers. Thus, each multicast packet with a certain TTL will have its TTL value decremented as it hops from router to router to reach its destination. Before the multicast packets hop over any mrouter, however, their TTL value has to be greater than the mrouter's threshold value. Thus, TTL acts as the energy of a Qmulticast-ip packet that gets decremented by 1 at each intervening mrouter hop. The TTL field may sometimes be decremented by large values under a global thresholding scheme provided to limit multicasts to sites and regions, if desired.

A TTL value of 16 limits the multicast traffic to an organizational LAN, as opposed to the values of 127 or 255, which send the associated multicast data traffic to the entire Internet MBone. TTL values between 16 through 127 are also allowed. It should be noted that these numbers are not randomly selected—they are reserved strictly for MBone usage. They have always been part of the IP protocol, but have never been used before the MBone.

Tunnels

The MBone is operationally supported through the mechanism of *tunneling*, a scheme to forward multicast packets among the islands of MBone subnets through legacy Internet IP routers (also referred to as *IP unicast routers*) that do not support IP multicast (see fig. 1.13). This is done by encapsulating the multicast packets inside regular IP packets. As a result, the intervening IP unicast routers see the multicast packets as unicast packets, thereby ensuring backward compatibility.

As the installed base of commercial hardware multicast routers increases, this mixed system of specially dedicated mrouters and tunnels will no longer be necessary. Most commercial router companies already support and ship multicast in their routers; therefore, it is expected that once they are deployed, the need for duplicate routers and tunnels will be eliminated.

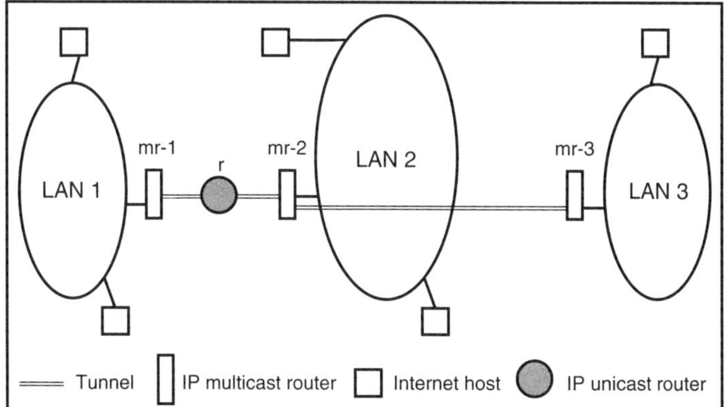

Figure 1.13

Tunnels can coexist with IP unicast and IP multicast routers.

The first multicast tunnel was established between Bolt, Beranek, and Newman, Inc. and Stanford University in the summer of 1988. Tunneling was originally meant to be just a short-term solution until the core Internet routers knew about IP multicasting. The term "tunneling" has come to stay, however, and is now an integral part of the MBone.

Truncated Tunnels

In the early phases of the MBone, IP multicast packets were routed on top of what is called *truncated tunnels*. In the truncated multicasting scheme, multicast group packets were forwarded to all the neighboring multicast routes, as long as the TTL of the packet was greater than the threshold value of the mrouter. As a result, mrouter nodes that did not express interest in receiving MBone traffic associated with a certain multicast group still received, and therefore routed, the traffic just because they happened to be within the sender's TTL range. This was obviously not a very efficient scheme, but provided a very useful initial test mechanism for the MBone.

Pruned Tunnels

Today, most tunnels are pruned. *Pruning* in multicasting is also referred to as *true multicasting*, which means that multicast packets are not forwarded to sites or mrouter nodes unless they have expressed an explicit interest in packets (via IGMP messages) belonging to that specific multicast group address, and are within the TTL range of the sender. Thus, the TTL/threshold scheme coupled with true multicasting provides a fairly efficient method for distributing and accessing the multicast media streams over the Internet.

Recent Media Coverage on the MBone

Recently, there has been a flurry of articles in the print media about the MBone. In a *New York Times* article entitled "Peering Out a Real-Time Window," writer Peter Lewis described IP multicasting as a technology that could take Internet users to the outer limits [16]. He claimed that the MBone might be the Information Superhighway itself, particularly with its capability to enable interactive audio and video across the Internet. The article clearly highlighted one of the major restrictions of the MBone—namely the bandwidth. The bandwidth is very limited, and therefore the use of the MBone for commercial purposes is also very limited at the time of this writing.

A *San Jose Mercury* article by David Bank, entitled "Agent Of Change," highlighted some of the commercial activities that are happening over the MBone [17]. The article mentioned Internet Multicasting Service—a commercial outfit that has been multicasting live programming over the MBone. Some of the noted events included the live multicast of floor debates in the House of Representatives and the U.S. Senate.

In an *Internet World Magazine* article called "Stretching the MBone: The Internet Broadcasting Network," Aaron Weiss gives an overview of the MBone and describes some of the MBone resources that are available on the Internet [18].

Chapter Summary

In this chapter, you have been given a very quick tour of the Internet and its associated TCP/IP protocol suite. You have also examined the different classes of Internet addresses, learning that the class D address is also called the multicast or group address. A small subset of this class D address space makes up what is called the MBone—a standard way of communicating simultaneously between multiple hosts over the Internet. Various features, like IP multicasting, TTL, mrouters, and tunnels, make up the important aspects of the MBone. The IGMP layer provides each desktop and the network routers the ability to join and leave a multicast group session on the MBone.

Network scalability of the MBone in terms of large-scale distribution of information in real-time explains the robustness in design. Some of the basic terms in network multimedia have been briefly discussed, especially relating to isochronous media audio and video. A large-scale delivery of time-based multimedia information will require a lightweight technology like IP multicasting.

In the next chapter, "The MBone Alternative: Life Beyond the Web," you will examine the potential benefits and limitations of using the MBone.

chapter 2

The MBone Alternative: Life Beyond the Web

Now that you have some technological background on the MBone, let's try to understand the potential benefits and limitations of using it. From the previous chapter, it is quite clear that the main benefit of using the MBone is the ability to distribute information to multiple recipients on the Internet. In this chapter, you will see how traditional ways of multiparty information communication compares to the MBone style of information distribution.

Internet Communication Models

Communication and sharing of information on the Internet is feasible in three different ways, as shown in figure 2.1.

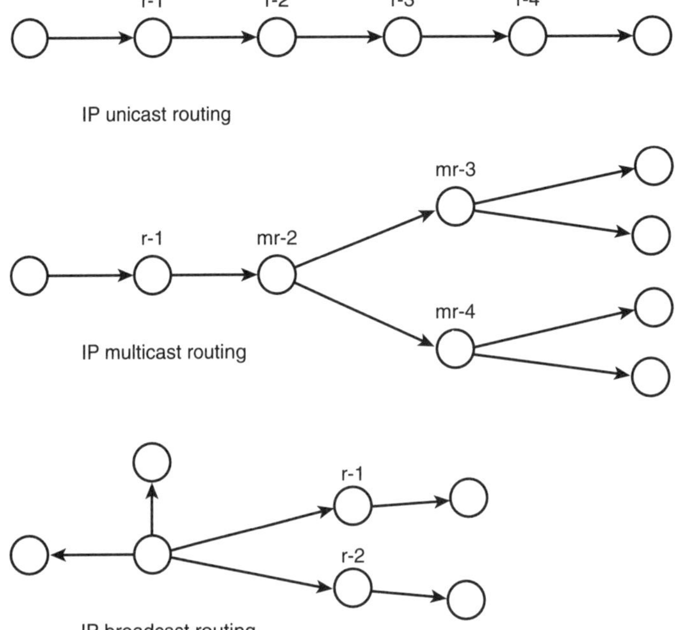

Figure 2.1

IP unicast, broadcast, and multicast routing examples.

For any fast multimedia communication between multiple sites, clearly IP unicast (point-to-point) and IP broadcast-based approaches are simply not enough. Both lead to either overloading the network or over-utilization of the participating hosts' CPU, neither of which is desirable. As explained before, the MBone uses the IP multicasting routing schemes to achieve fast, real-time, multiparty communication in an efficient manner.

Information Distribution Media Today

Several information access and distribution media are available today, such as cable TV, telephones, magazines and books, the World Wide Web, Lotus Notes, e-mail, and so on.

Information access and distribution mechanisms can be separated into two models, as follows:

- **"You go to the information source" model**—The World Wide Web, magazines, and book stores are good examples of this model. In this situation, it is the responsibility of the interested consumer to find and then access the information. The creators of the information just wait for interested consumers to visit their information kiosk and access the desired information.
- **"The information source comes to you" model**—Cable TV is a good example of this model. Cable movies and other entertainment information are beamed to users in their homes. Consumers, on the other hand, do not have to try hard (with the exception of changing channels) to access the information—the information is delivered directly to the home (or is it the couch?).

Traditional Cable TV and the MBone

Cable TV is one of the premier information providers to most homes, offices, and individuals. The alliance of entertainment content providers along with cable companies have invested heavily in laying down the infrastructure for distribution of multimedia information. This infrastructure includes studios for content creation, switches for distribution of multimedia programs, TV sets, coaxial TV cables to every home, and so on. Multimedia content that is created at the studios is delivered to each home in a *uni-directional* (or one-way) manner—therefore, the home user cannot interact with the information delivered (see fig. 2.2).

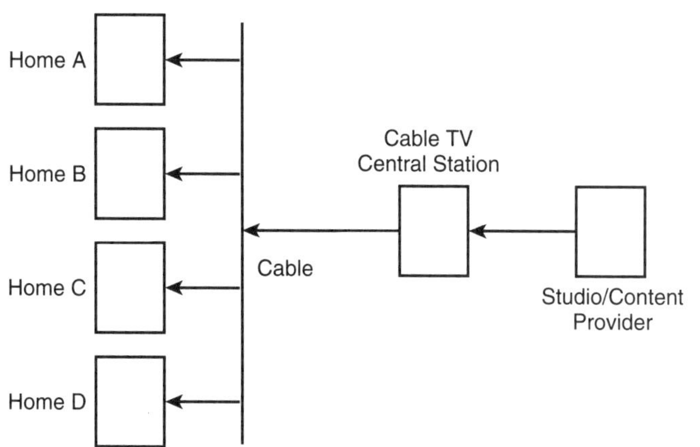

Figure 2.2

The uni-directional flow of information in the cable TV model.

The information content in today's cable TV system is analog in nature. The cost of producing and transmitting the content is exorbitantly high, but the quality is also very high. This includes the quality of rendering video media on cable TV (greater than or equal to 30 frames per second) and audio media (surround sound quality).

The Nature of the MBone

The MBone makes some of the cable TV models potentially feasible over the Internet. Such things were hard to fathom a few years ago before the MBone was invented. As of today, the MBone is being used for transmitting and receiving live interactive multimedia programming over the Internet. The information that flows over the MBone is digital in nature (like most information on the Internet), and every consumer has the potential to be a producer as well. In addition, the nature of the MBone infrastructure is such that it is possible to make multimedia information *two-way interactive*—that is, the consumer of the information can interact with the information delivered (see fig. 2.3). The cost of production on the MBone, however, is not as prohibitive as in the cable TV world—of course, this cost does not reflect the quality of production.

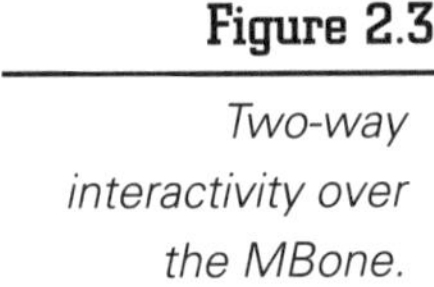

Figure 2.3

Two-way interactivity over the MBone.

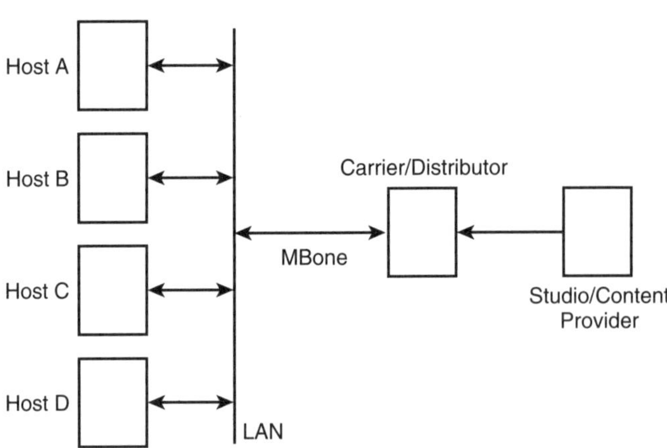

An amateur level multimedia production for transmission over the MBone involves costs at various levels, as depicted in table 2.1.

Table 2.1

Approximate Costs in Transmitting Amateur Programming Over the MBone

Programming Method	Approximate Cost (in U.S. Dollars)
Computer workstation	$10,000.00
Video digitizer	$1000.00
Video camera	$1000.00
Microphone with speakers	$100.00
Internet connectivity (T-1)	$10,000.00

Note that in the figure 2.3, consumers on Hosts A through D not only receive multimedia information from the information provider, but can also transmit information for others. Thus, Host A can not only view the information that is being beamed by the content provider, but can also transmit its own content from Host A to Hosts B through D and the content provider—all over the MBone. The role of producers and consumers can be switched with relative ease.

Potential Uses for the MBone

Will the MBone affect the outreach of cable TV? In other words, will the MBone add to or compete against the number of cable TV subscribers? The answer is hard to predict, but in this author's humble opinion—probably not. Recently, entertainment, cable, phone, and computer companies have formed alliances to provide better quality programming to homes and offices. The variety of services that are being looked into include the following:

- TV (basic, subscription, and pay-per-view)
- Interactive games (single and multiuser)
- Video on-demand
- Home shopping
- Banking and financial transaction services
- Digital music audio
- Electronically delivered newspapers and magazines
- Long distance education (corporate and classroom training)

Delivering such a myriad of services will require an overhaul or redesign of current TV systems and architecture [1] (see bibliography). The alliance might help merge the existing analog TV systems with digital technologies, however. For example, the MBone can facilitate some of the aspects of two-way, large-scale media delivery; cable TV systems, on the other hand, can provide the much needed bandwidth or network resources to the MBone. Thus, an integrated system might look similar to that shown in figure 2.4.

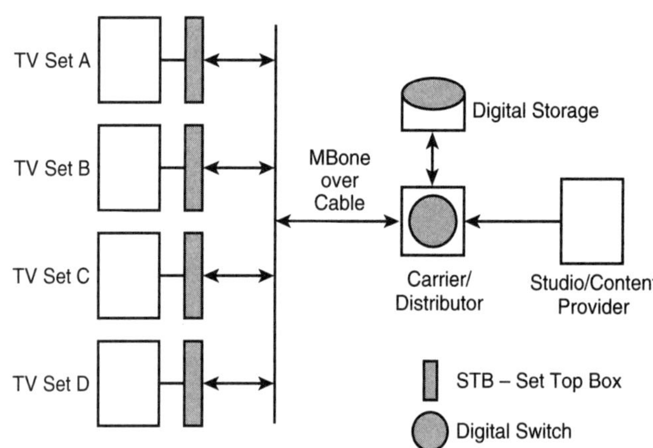

Figure 2.4

A potential convergence of the analog cable systems and the digital MBone.

In the figure 2.4, notice the two changes as compared to figure 2.3:

- The *Set Top Box* (STB) unit in every home TV set
- The digital switch at the carrier or cable company site

STBs will perform a variety of functions, such as providing interactivity with home viewers, video audio compression and decompression, and digital to analog signal conversion. Such STB units are already available in the market; one example is the Magic Carpet product from a Bay Area computer company, Silicon Graphics, Inc. The digital switch will provide some of the similar features at the provider end. Several such designs are already being investigated and built by corporations, universities, and research labs all around the world—the question is no longer *if* these designs will be built, but *how soon* they will be delivered.

World Wide Web and the MBone

The *World Wide Web* (WWW) was invented by Tim Berners-Lee at CERN Physics Laboratory in Switzerland in 1989. The *National Center for Supercomputing Applications* (NCSA) of the University of Illinois later produced a browser client for the Web called Mosaic. Mosaic revolutionized the use and acceptance of Internet by the non-academic population all over the world. The growth of the World Wide Web has been phenomenal so far, as can be seen in figure 2.5.

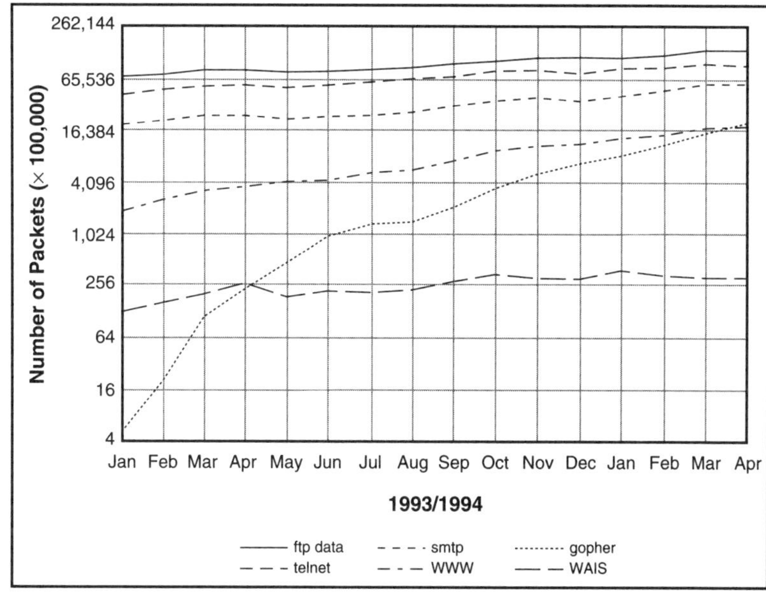

Figure 2.5

The growth of the World Wide Web during 1993 and 1994.

The architecture of the World Wide Web as it exists today is based on a client/server model (see fig. 2.6). A *client/server model* is one in which the server becomes a repository of information, and the client is a vehicle to view and access that repository. An information provider can create documents as files and store them on a server, which is also connected to the Internet or the internal company LAN. Any potential consumer of the information on the Internet can request and view those documents using a client or browser software such as Mosaic.

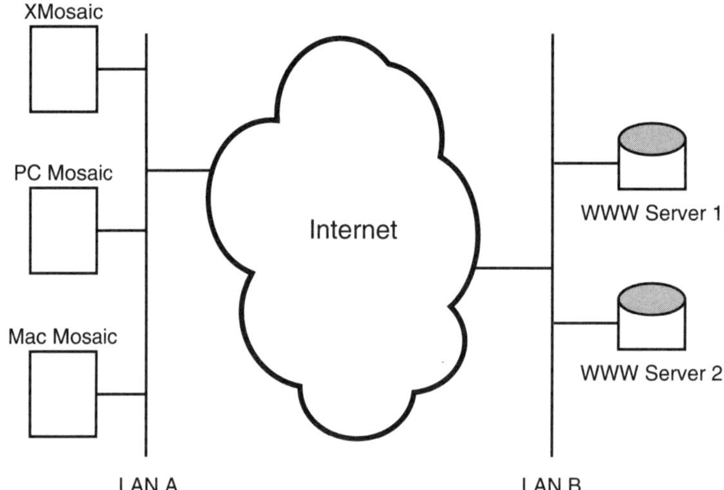

Figure 2.6

The client/server architecture of the World Wide Web.

The Web Model of Information Distribution

In the World Wide Web, information gets delivered to clients only when they request delivery—the servers themselves cannot decide to deliver to a client. The model is more like the "You go to the information source" model discussed earlier in this chapter, and not the other way around. The Web model of information distribution is similar to the newspaper and magazine model, where you go to the store to view the newspaper or magazine, read it, and later buy it.

Most of the MBone applications today follow the "Information source comes to you" model, much like the TV model. So, is there a synergistic relationship here between the Web and the MBone? Or does one subsume the other? In the author's opinion, both models can and probably will coexist, much like in the non-online world. In the near future, however, a few sample application prototypes have been demonstrated where some level of integration of World Wide Web and the MBone is quite visible. One of the integration models that has been developed and proposed by the author clearly shows how the WWW and MBone could be tightly integrated for better information delivery on the Internet. This specific project, called Shared Mosaic, is described in detail in Chapter 4, "MBone Multimedia Applications."

Groupware and the MBone

The term *groupware* essentially means a piece of technology that enables effective group work. In more elaborate terms, groupware is a piece of software or hardware that facilitates a group of individuals to work together as a team. Groupware technologies are also sometimes known as *collaboration technologies*. Groupware is subdivided into several categories—one such way to define these categories is depicted in figure 2.7.

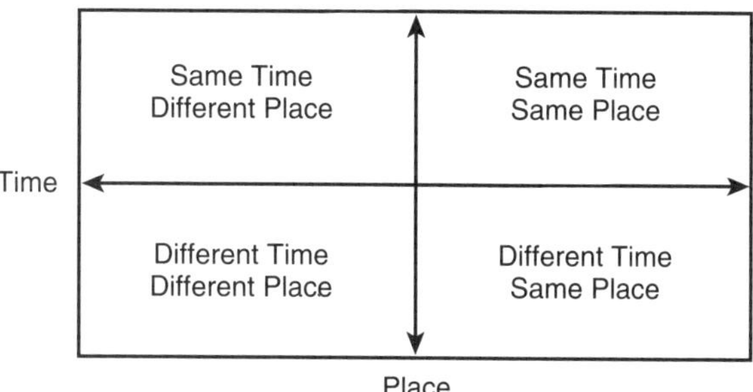

Figure 2.7

The various forms of groupware models.

Different technologies enable each of the categories shown in figure 2.7. For example, e-mail communication-based technology will fit into the Different Time, Different Place model of collaboration, because each user involved in the collaboration can read, compose, and reply to the e-mail at different times, and the participants involved could be physically distributed. Similarly, an example of Same Time, Different Place groupware (also called *real-time* or *synchronous collaboration*) could be a desktop video conferencing system. Such a collaboration system enables people in different physical locations to work together only when each individual is available at his or her desktop at the same time. The MBone of today facilitates some of the Different Place, Same Time groupware models.

The Effectiveness of Groupware

It has been shown in several experiments [5], research studies [6], and usage of synchronous groupware technologies [7] that presence of computer desktop-based voice and video conferencing technologies greatly enhance the effectiveness of distance collaborations. The free flow of ideas through informal voice conversations, along with seeing each other's body and face gestures, greatly help in preserving the human aspects of such electronic remote collaborations.

Groupware Products and Standards

Several meeting-oriented groupware tools are available in the market. The specifications of these vary from one product to another, sometimes quite drastically. Standards again will be defined at various levels as the process itself, which was shown in figure 1.6 and table 1.1 in the previous chapter—that is, at the level of media encoding and decoding, compression algorithms, and networking. Users must consider the standards at each of the different levels. For example, in a video conferencing system, the specifications shown in table 2.2 might range from NTSC, PAL, and HDTV video formats for encoding and decoding, MPEG, NetVideo, H.261 for compression, and *International Telecommunications Union* (ITU)/H.320, *Real-Time Protocol* (RTP) MBone for networking [12].

Table 2.2

Specifications for Audio and Video Over Computer Networks

Medium Type	Encoding/Decoding	Compression	Networking
Audio	8-bit, 8 KHz telephone quality	PCM (Pulse Code Modulation)	RTP/MB one ITU-H.320 ITU-T.120
	16-bit, 44.1 KHz CD quality	ADPCM, LPC, GSM	
Video	NTSC (30 fps)	JPEG, MPEG	RTP/MB one
	PAL (25 fps)	NetVideo, H.261	ITU-H.320
	HDTV (60 fps)		ITU-T.120

There are a number of products available in the market today that follow the ITU-T.120 data conferencing and H.320-based video conferencing specifications. These products do not require the Internet for use—they use the *Plain Old Telephone System* (POTS). These systems work over existing analog phone lines or the *Integrated Services Digital Network* (ISDN). A list of such products is included in Appendix B, "The MBone Products Shopping Guide." It is important to note, however, that these systems mainly support point-to-point communication between two parties—although a very limited number do support more than two participants, these products never support a large number of participants.

Groupware applications such as video, audio, and data conferencing on the MBone, however, can exploit the power of IP multicasting. As a result, MBone groupware applications are scalable to allow and support hundreds and even thousands of simultaneous participants in a multimedia conference. This obviously raises a few pertinent issues related to the use and benefits of the MBone today and in the future. In addition, the question of how these MBone-compliant applications and services will work with non-MBone compliant ones is also raised. All of these issues are discussed in the next section.

MBone Issues

In March 1992, the MBone was first used over DARTNet, a small segment of the Internet, to conduct a meeting using real-time audio and video. Some of the participants in that meeting were geographically distributed, but participated via the MBone. Since then, the MBone has continued to grow in its installed base, as well as in its uses. Most users today are the sophisticated Internet users such as corporations, academic universities, and research organizations.

Current Uses of the MBone

The MBone is currently used for hosting public events, workshops, seminars, classroom courses, IETF meetings, private meetings that span multiple continents and organizations, and a few news and entertainment events.

In the past, completely commercial events—from the Rolling Stones' live concert, to scientific NASA space shuttle launches, to Dr. Robert Ballard's annual odysseys from under the ocean—have been multicasted on the MBone.

In addition to the Internet-wide uses of the MBone, the MBone works very well within the boundaries of corporate internal LANs. This means that multimedia traffic will not go over to the larger Internet MBone. Consider the situation shown in figure 2.8, which consists of two LANs within an organization.

The MBone can be easily created within the organization. If the *Time To Live* (TTL) of an MBone session is limited to 16 or less, then the MBone data traffic stays within the same LAN as the source of the traffic. For example, if the MBone session was created at Host 1 on LAN A, then a TTL of 16 or less will keep the MBone traffic within LAN A. The TTL value can be raised, however, so that the MBone data feed goes over the Router I to the hosts on LAN B, but does not cross over to the larger Internet over Router E.

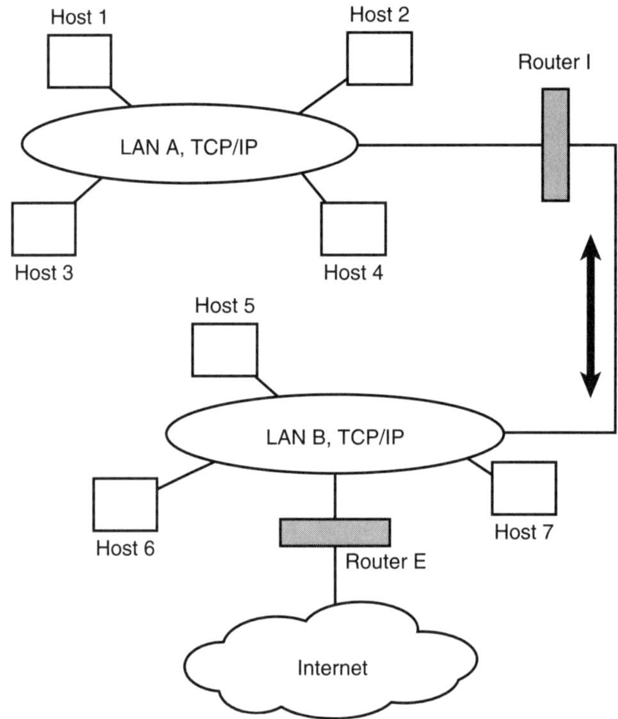

Figure 2.8

Two LANs within an organization, running TCP/IP and interconnected via Router I.

Benefits of the MBone

The MBone enables multicast of multimedia streams to multiple hosts simultaneously—it is not a broadcast scheme. The multicast traffic on the MBone flows over Internet IP routers and enhanced IP multicast routers, and then to the hosts that are interested in receiving the traffic. Thus, it is clear that it is an interest-based scheme for routing multicast packets. The IGMP layer in the TCP/IP stack shown in the previous chapter enables users of multimedia applications to express an interest in accessing multimedia data streams for the MBone.

In addition to the technical benefits of the MBone to multimedia application developers, the MBone also provides several benefits to the user community. The primary use of the MBone today is based on several applications that are described in Chapter 4. Without going into details of these tools now, let's briefly delve into what it takes to transmit or receive the MBone media streams from your computer desktop.

A minimum configuration involves a multimedia computer connected to the Internet. A multimedia computer consists of a color display, an audio/video digitizer card, a video camera, a microphone, a speaker, and MBone software. Any user on the MBone can reserve from their desktop an MBone channel or session. This is done programmatically, and in most cases, an MBone session is reserved immediately on demand. There are no central authorities, per se, for processing such requests. An MBone channel or session is characterized by the parameters shown in table 2.3.

Table 2.3

Parameters for Specifying an MBone Session

MBone Session Parameters	Parameter Values
Session/channel name	CNBC Internet security interview
Multicast address	224.2.253.125
Media type(s)	Audio, video, document
Media parameter(s)	Media encodings, compression, application names
Media port(s)	4545
Range/scope (TTL)	127
Password for security	timbak126~

Such sessions can be received by others on the MBone if they choose to do so. These MBone sessions, and the associated multimedia traffic, are not routed to hosts and sites that are not interested in receiving the traffic.

Paying for the MBone

So who pays for this fine luxury? MBone users do not pay anything extra for using the MBone—in return, however, they do not get guarantees of *Quality of Service* (QoS) rendered to them; this is also called *best effort service.* The system that includes the computer desktop, and the Internet network service for all the participants involved in the session, does the best it can do to deliver the MBone service, but without any assurances. There are, however, no *denial of service* attacks, which means that the system will always provide a service, but it will not necessarily guarantee the quality of that service. Essentially, the system always attempts to provide a service, no matter how poor the service is. The MBone service is provided by the *Internet Service Providers* (ISPs) as part of the Internet connectivity to their customers (see fig. 2.9).

Figure 2.9

The MBone service coexisting with Internet connectivity.

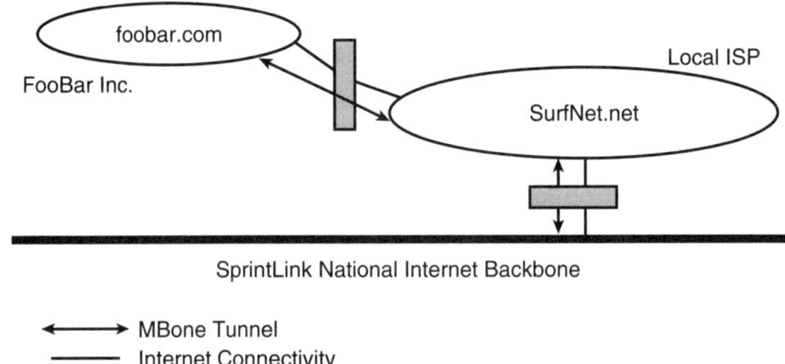

Management of the MBone

The Internet, as well as the MBone, has grown beyond the U.S. national boundaries. Therefore, a central control like the *Federal Communications Commission* (FCC) might not be feasible. As of today, there is no central management authority that controls the day-to-day happenings on the MBone. There is, however, a community of users and developers of the MBone that oversee the engineering and operational issues. The community spans across multiple countries and organizations, and their primary mode of overseeing is via the Internet mailing list.

The MBone is a jointly owned resource of the community, and therefore care is taken in not misutilizing it. Misuse comes mainly from overuse—none of the users are paying anything extra for such high-quality use. Unfortunately, however, there is no way to stop a miscreant from misusing the MBone without paying a fair share for the use (or misuse). The MBone has provided a powerful ability to distribute such live multimedia streams to desktops worldwide. Such power has traditionally existed in the hands of big corporate houses like the cable networks and Hollywood production houses, and comes with a heavy price tag.

Proper infrastructure is now being put into place on the Internet that will enable individuals to request and reserve network bandwidth for a certain price. The price will reflect the use of resources and the QoS rendered by the MBone. This mechanism may curb the overuse or misuse of the network resources, and hopefully users will pay for their fair share of use.

Multimedia Producers and the MBone

The MBone has created a lot of demand for bandwidth, as more and more companies and organizations are connecting to the MBone. In the process, they are upgrading their Internet connectivity infrastructure to participate in the MBone. The programming content variety today is very limited, although interesting programming continues to evolve. For example, a 24-hour world radio network that multicasts international news from around the world recently came online on the MBone. This was well-received by the MBone community worldwide because the contents were relevant to the audience. Another program called the Internet Town Hall meeting, which multicasts audio feed from the U.S. Senate, is multicast on the MBone only for the U.S. audience. Various other programs are also multicasted from time to time—however, the producers of such programs make sure that not all of them are distributing their content simultaneously. This is due to the very limited network resources available today—only 500 Kbps worth of the Internet backbone is allocated for transmission of the MBone multimedia at any given time.

MBone video today is not quite real-time, and therefore might not be able to compete against what is available on cable TV, where frame rates of 5–10 fps are the norm. The same video, however, might give much better performance within corporate networks. Some of the experimental test beds like the *Bay Area Gigabit Network* (BAGNet) in the U.S. and SuperJanet in the U.K. have shown the potential of delivering lots of full-motion video streams over the MBone. These test beds use the MBone over high-speed gigabit *Asynchronous Transfer Mode* (ATM) networks.

In contrast to video, MBone audio is near real-time. Audio multicasting gives near-telephone-quality voice. Because the MBone is still in the process of becoming real instead of virtual, however, minor glitches and dropouts might sometimes be seen in multimedia feed.

MBone Bandwidth and Censorship

As of today, there is only limited bandwidth available on the MBone for use—500 Kbps at any given time. Even this network resource use does not come for an extra price. The opinions on whether to pay extra are still quite varied.

Internet users who do not appreciate any multimedia production on the MBone will always exist. Most users today, however, are concerned about the overuse of the limited network resources—therefore, it is not so much as censorship, per se, as it is the limited available resources. The MBone is as open as any other Internet information distribution medium in that it is not regulated by any central authority, like radio, TV, and cable waves are regulated by the FCC. The MBone is a resource of the community that is managed by the MBone users and developers themselves in an open distributed manner.

Interesting multimedia programming coupled with the power of the MBone is likely to create heavy demand for better infrastructure. Telephone and cable companies will lay down larger bandwidth to every home and office. Newer upcoming technologies, such as the *Resource Reservation Protocol* (RSVP) [11], will, once deployed over the larger Internet, make commercial multimedia over the MBone a reality. Bandwidth will be available on demand with QoS guarantees for a price.

Although each individual will have the power to create the best multimedia content on his or her desktop, it is not clear how soon network bandwidth will be commoditized. Distributing multimedia programming over the MBone will require advance reservation of network bandwidth between all the participating sites. In addition, each participating site might have to pay either for transmitting or receiving the content.

Large cable TV networks will tend to buy lots of bandwidth and might tie up most of the network resources. Buying just enough bandwidth to distribute multimedia content may be cheap; however, buying lots of bandwidth with high QoS for indefinite amounts of time will still be expensive. Unlike large cable TV networks, small multimedia content providers might use the necessary bandwidth for short durations of time on demand, and distribute their rich content from their desktop studio to a paying audience on the Internet.

Chapter Summary

In this chapter, you have examined the potential benefits and limitations of the MBone. IP multicasting, the underlying principle behind the MBone, facilitates large-scale distribution of multimedia content. As a result, the MBone might bring about a convergence between the cable TV world, Internet technologies, POTS telephony, and the desktop computers.

Groupware products are very popular, but do not scale for community use because of the unicast TCP-oriented communication schemes on which they are built. IP multicasting enables groupware developers to build more network-scalable solutions for use by large number of simultaneous users.

It is quite easy to create, manage, distribute, and access multimedia content over the MBone at an amateur level; however, more infrastructure support like the RSVP is needed to make the MBone commercial. Network resource reservation and allocation, combined with guarantees on QoS and proper payment and billing schemes for the multimedia content distribution over the MBone, will help MBone scale in the marketplace.

c h a p t e r 3

A View Inside the MBone

Traditionally, software developers have designed interactive multimedia applications based on one of the following criteria:

- ➜ Proprietary transport protocols that run on dial-up phone lines
- ➜ Open protocols such as the ITU H.320 that run on dial-up telephone networks
- ➜ Open protocols that use unicast IP as the transport mechanism

Interactive applications on the Internet have traditionally used unicast TCP/IP as the network transport—that is, until the MBone came along. Most applications that are available today support point-to-point multimedia interactions between two sites, but they do not scale well in multiparty, multihost scenarios. As more and more sites connect to an ongoing multimedia session, the performance in terms of network traffic generated, as well as the speed of interaction, degrades considerably. For more information on network scalability, see Chapter 2, "The MBone Alternative: Life Beyond the Web."

The real-time multimedia data streams require fast transports with low overheads, such as the *User Datagram Protocol* (UDP), and TCP-based schemes do not scale very well in these situations. One of the main reasons that UDP exists as an alternative to TCP is to support real-time applications. One of the primary reasons that UDP exists as an alternative to CTP is to support fast, real-time applications.

The UDP protocol is unreliable in nature, and therefore does not guarantee ordered and reliable delivery. This means that at times, the information packets may reach the destination in an order different from the way in which they were sent, or they may not reach the destination at all. It has been demonstrated by several MBone applications, however, that with proper programming support at the application level, both ordered and reliable delivery can be achieved without much trouble. A major advantage of using UDP/IP is that the UDP data checksum is optional—this is needed to support real-time applications that can tolerate some bit damage, but cannot tolerate the delays of repair from TCP-style retransmissions. End-to-end acknowledgment schemes like TCP don't scale well to large multicast group communications (i.e., the "ack implosion" problem).

In this chapter, you explore in detail the internal technical details and various flavors of MBone technology, IP multicast addressing, and the multicast packet routing.

Shared Responsibility: The MBone

Most of the MBone applications scale very well to support interactive multimedia for both the point-to-point setting and the multiparty scenario. The MBone uses IP multicasting for distributing media streams using UDP transmissions with relatively low overheads. In a multihost setting, distribution of packets is no longer the responsibility of each participating IP host; it becomes the joint distributed responsibility of intervening IP routers.

As shown in figure 3.1, Sender A on subnet "foo.com" can distribute information packets to Receivers B through E without making four copies of it. The replication occurs at the high-end multicast routers maintained by the MBone service providers. In this case, it is mr2 that receives the sender's information packets over the tunnel, replicates into two copies, and forwards each copy over the two outgoing tunnels to subnets "bar.com" and "foobar.com." The subnet multicast routers mr3 and mr4 then take the responsibility of forwarding the information packets to interested receivers on the respective subnets.

The topology of tunnels over the MBone has been designed in such a way that no multicast router has a fanout of more than four outgoing tunnels. This way, the overhead involved in replicating and routing the packets over each tunnel is reduced to an optimal value for real-time communications.

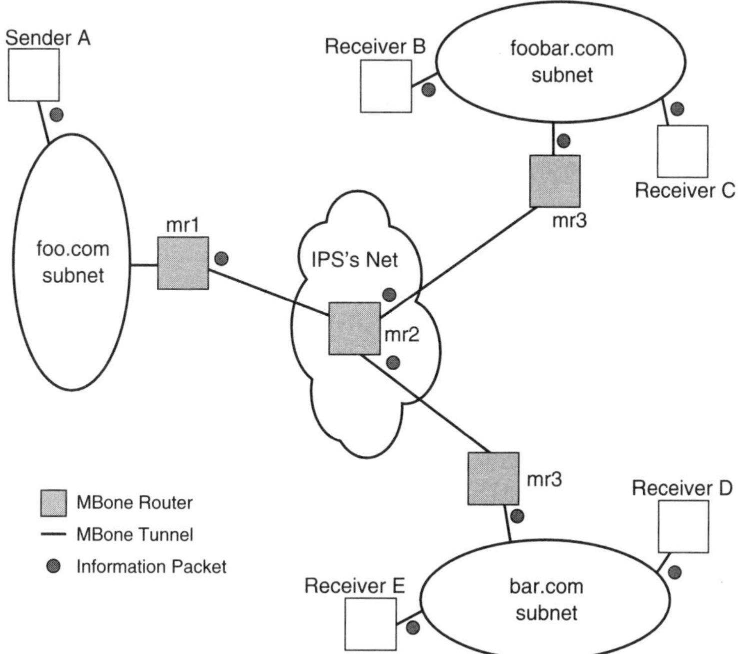

Figure 3.1

The routing of multicast packets over the MBone.

The reliability and fidelity of rendered multimedia at participating receiving sites is achieved via application-level receiver-side adaptation—that is, in the event of congestion and packet loss on Internet routes, the applications can still recover gracefully. Several MBone multimedia tools that use this paradigm of rendering and distributing multimedia are described in Chapter 4, "MBone Multimedia Applications."

IP Multicasting and the IGMP

In previous chapters, the terms IP multicast address, IP multicasting, and IGMP were mentioned briefly. Now each of these terms will be discussed in more detail.

The multicast group addresses (also called class D addresses) range from 224.0.0.0 to 239.255.255.255. The multicast router refuses to forward any multicast datagram with a destination address between 224.0.0.0 and 224.0.0.255, inclusive, regardless of its *Time To Live* (TTL). The address 224.0.0.0 is guaranteed not to be assigned to any group, and 224.0.0.1 is assigned to the permanent group of all IP multicast systems. 224.0.0.1 is used to address all IP multicast systems on the directly connected network.

Internet routing protocols such as the *Routing Information Protocol* (RIP) and the *Open Shortest Path First* (OSPF) protocol have traditionally been used by IP routers to find a path for IP packets from source to destination. The *Internet Group Management Protocol* (IGMP) is used for routers to learn the existence of members on their directly attached subnets. The header fields in an IGMP message looks like that shown in figure 3.2.

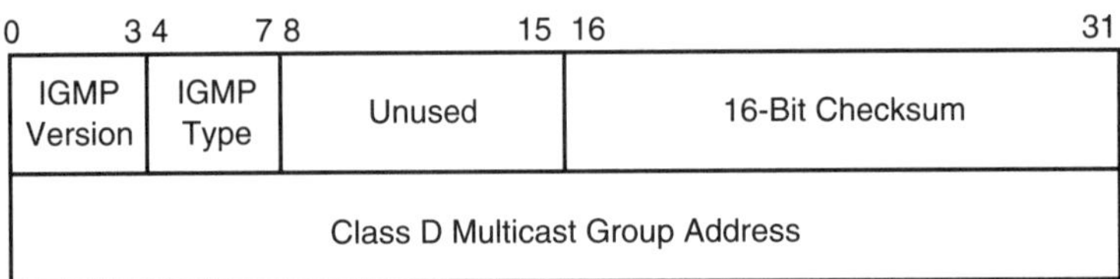

Figure 3.2

An 8-byte IGMP message showing header information.

IGMP is used to keep neighboring multicast routers informed of the host group memberships present on a particular local network. Thus, an IP host on a local subnet informs the neighboring multicast router about the different multicast groups to which it belongs. To support IGMP, the host must join the "all-systems" group (address 224.0.0.1) on each network interface, and must remain a member for as long as the host is up and running.

The messages addressed to "224.0.0.1" are not forwarded beyond the local subnet. The multicast routers recognize this address and do not forward these packets, regardless of the TTL value of the packet. This packet traffic thus does not hop out of your subnet—it stays within your local area subnet.

The IGMP messages consist primarily of three message types, as follows:

- Type 1: Group membership queries
- Type 2: Group membership reports
- Type 3: *Distance Vector Multicasting Routing Protocol* (DVMRP) routing updates

Several other types of messages have also been defined, such as IGMP PIM, IGMP MOSPF, IGMP CBT, and IGMP MTRACE. The IGMP membership query messages are generated by an mrouter on multicast-capable subnets, and sent to the 224.0.0.1 group to trigger group membership updates. In return, end-hosts generate IGMP membership reports for active multicast groups and send them to the destination multicast group. Both the query and report packets are generated with a TTL of 1; thus, neither of these message types are propagated beyond the local subnet (see fig. 3.3).

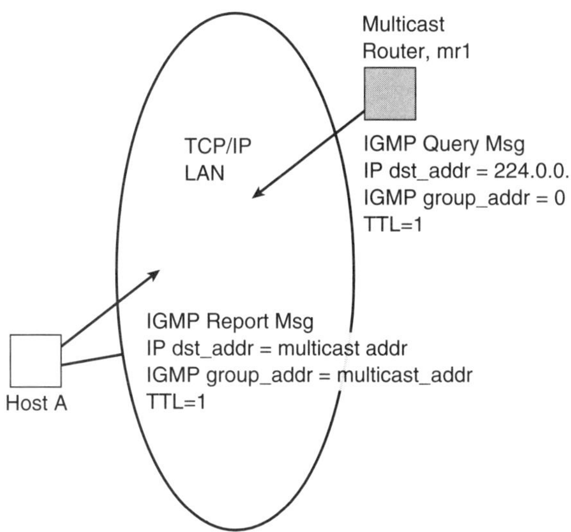

Figure 3.3

IGMP Query and Report Messages within a local subnet.

The IGMP DVMRP updates exchanged between neighboring multicast routers present two distinct cases. Messages exchanged between *multicast routers* (mrouters) connected via a multicast-capable subnet are sent to the 224.0.0.4 multicast group, whereas neighbors connected via a tunnel use unicast updates between tunnel endpoints. The multicast DVMRP updates are sent with a TTL of 1, and therefore are not propagated beyond the local subnet.

DVMRP is only one of the mechanisms for routing multicast traffic; other algorithms do exist as well, and will be described in later sections of the chapter.

MBone Tunneling Schemes

An IP multicast source on an end-host generates standard UDP data packets, with the exception that the standard unicast IP destination address is replaced by a class D multicast address. These packets are then transmitted on a local multicast-capable subnet, and it is the responsibility of the mrouters to forward these packets along the proper multicast distribution path. The mroute-enabled IP routers in the current MBone have led to the use of tunneling between multicast-capable islands, as shown in figure 3.4.

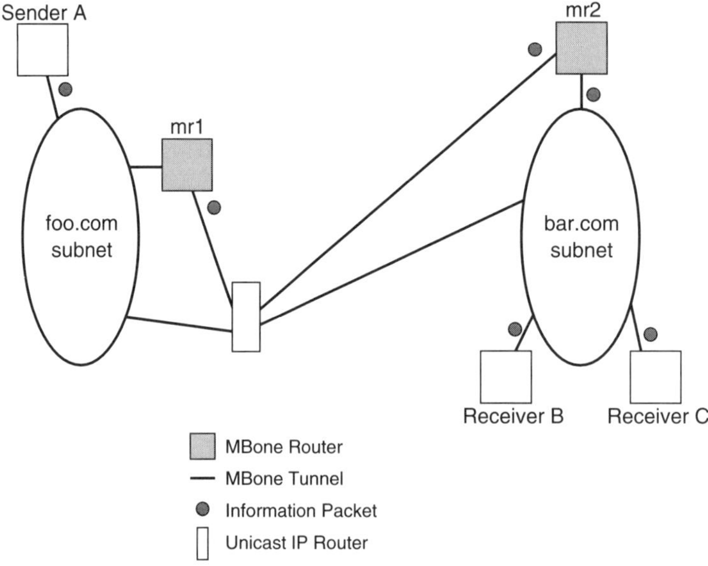

Figure 3.4

A virtual point-to-point link created using a tunnel.

Source Routed and Encapsulated Tunneling

Two forms of tunneling have been used by the MBone—those using an IP Loose Source Route (LSRR) option called *source routed* (or in short srcrt) tunnels, and those using IP-in-IP Encapsulation called *encapsulated* tunnels. IP multicast packets traversing an encapsulated tunnel are characterized by their IP source and destination addresses being the IP addresses of the tunnel endpoint multicast routers.

The srcrt'ed tunnel packets are more difficult to identify. They have an IP destination address, which is the tunnel destination endpoint, and an IP option, which is the LSRR (a special type of IP packet). These tunnel packets contain two recorded IP addresses—the first being the tunnel source endpoint, and the second being the multicast destination group.

Most of the MBone tunnels on the Internet today are encapsulated tunnels. The srcrt'ed tunnels were phased out because they are not an efficient way to send packets—they cause too much processing overhead at each router. The current mrouter implementations, however, are quite backward compatible with the srcrt'ed mrouters.

Multicast Addresses and the TTL

To send a multicast datagram, specify an IP multicast address in the range 224.0.0.0 to 239.255.255.255 as the destination address in a sendto() call. Each multicast group address is also characterized with a scoping value called the *Time To Live* or TTL, mentioned previously. TTL refers to the normal TTL field in the IP header.

By default, IP multicast datagrams are sent with a TTL of 1, which prevents them from being forwarded beyond a single subnetwork.

Multicast datagrams with a TTL of zero will not be transmitted on any subnet, but may be delivered locally if the sending host belongs to the destination group, and if multicast loopback has not been disabled on the sending socket. Multicast datagrams with a TTL greater than one may be delivered to more than one subnet if there are one or more multicast routers attached to the first-hop subnet. To provide meaningful scope control, the multicast routers support the notion of TTL thresholds, which prevent datagrams with less than a certain TTL from traversing certain subnets.

Consider, for example, the following configuration specified by the file /etc/mrouted.conf for a DVMRP multicast router on a subnet "foo.com":

```
tunnel 196.205.123.56 126.112.45.29 metric 1 threshold 32
```

Thus, any multicast packet that originates from a host on the same subnet as "foo.com" must have a TTL of more than 32 before the mrouter can route the packet beyond the local subnet. If the TTL is greater than 32, then the mrouter will decrement the TTL value by one before forwarding the packet along the distribution tree.

Truncated and Pruned Multicasting

Both of these terms are used for multicast routing paradigms. In *truncated multicasting*, the multicast traffic gets routed to the distribution path based on the TTL of the packet and the threshold of the tunnel. If the tunnel threshold is less than the TTL on the packet, the mrouter forwards the packet down the path after decrementing the TTL by one.

In *pruned multicasting*, however, there are two levels for scoping multicast traffic. One level, of course, is based on the TTL and threshold values, and the other is based on proper management of IGMP-based interest mechanism. For the latter, if no host on a subnet expresses an interest in receiving specific multicast group traffic, then no multicast data traffic comes over the tunnel to the subnet, regardless of the TTL value attached to the multicast group data packets. Traffic only flows over links that have active receivers attached to them. This clearly is a better scheme and results in less unwanted multicast traffic to and from your subnet—pruned multicasting is also called *true multicasting* for this reason. The MBone is now in an upgrade mode to deploy pruned multicast-based routers. The majority of mrouters, however, are still based on the old software that supports only truncated multicasting. The DVMRP multicast routers (version 3.x and later) support the pruning feature.

Multicast Routing Flavors

Multicast packets are routed from one point to another over the MBone via what is called a multicast routing protocol. A *multicast routing protocol* is a set of standards and parameters that two endpoints of communication agree on to route packets. To route the class D IP multicast group addressed packets between different IP subnets, several routing schemes have been developed and deployed on the MBone. These routing protocol flavors are now Internet standards and widely deployed inside the routers. Two endpoints may use different routing protocol standards, but still interoperate with each other, thanks to the developers of the routing engine software and hardware.

Distance Vector Multicast Routing Protocol

To route the class D multicast group addressed packets between different subnets, several routing schemes have been developed and deployed on the MBone. One of the first routing mechanisms that was developed by Steve Deering of Xerox PARC is called *Distance Vector Multicast Routing Protocol* (DVMRP). It is the distance-vector (based on hop-counts) routing protocol implemented by the mrouted program that is available as part of the IP multicast operating system kernel extensions. An earlier version of DVMRP is specified in RFC-1075 [8] (see bibliography). The version implemented in mrouted today, however, is quite different from what is specified in that RFC.

The DVMRP-based multicast router maintains topological knowledge via a distance-vector routing protocol—such as the *Routing Information Protocol* (RIP), described in RFC-1058—upon which it implements a multicast forwarding algorithm called Truncated Reverse Path Broadcasting. DVMRP-based routers are available at various FTP sites and also available commercially from Alantec Corporation.

Multicast Open Shortest Path First

MOSPF is the IP multicast extension to the *Open Shortest Path First* (OSPF) IP routing protocol. OSPF routing is based on link-state, as opposed to RIP, which is based on hop-counts. John Moy has implemented MOSPF for the Proteon routers. Proteon Inc. is one of the companies that sells MOSPF-based multicast routers. A network of routers running MOSPF can forward IP multicast packets directly, sending no more than one copy over any link, and without the need for any tunnels.

Protocol Independent Multicasting

When group members, and senders to those group members, are distributed sparsely across a wide area, both these schemes are not very efficient. Multicast data traffic (in DVMRP) or membership report information (in MOSPF) are periodically sent over many links that do not lead to receivers or senders, respectively. Also, both of these routing schemes were designed for use within regions where a group is widely represented and/or plenty of bandwidth is available.

Protocol Independent Multicasting (PIM) [14] is a recent development in the IETF Network Working Group. The goal of PIM is to be able to route multicast packets without being dependent on the underlying unicast IP routing schemes like DVMRP (based on RIP) and MOSPF (based on OSPF). In addition, a goal of PIM is to take care of some of the scaling issues with respect to wide-area sparse use of the MBone. PIM, therefore, has two modes—Sparse Mode PIM and Dense Mode PIM. *Sparse Mode PIM* is a multicast protocol that is optimized for a group that is distributed across different regions of the Internet. *Dense Mode PIM*, on the other hand, is optimized for groups that are located in a close proximity.

Some IP router vendors, such as Cisco Systems and 3Com Corporation, along with their engineers, are spearheading the development and deployment of PIM-based multicast routers on the MBone. These routers understand IP multicast packets in their native mode; therefore, tunnels are no longer required to route traffic between each other. These routers, however, do use tunneling when speaking to nonnative DVMRP-based IP multicast routers.

PIM, MOSPF, and DVMRP implementations of multicast routing interoperate with each other. As a result, the PIM-based subnets can be interlinked quite seamlessly with DVMRP tunnels and MOSPF subnets.

The Private MBone

Over the years, many curious individuals and organizations have asked, "Can we set up a private or local MBone?" The simple answer is "Yes!" You do have to be careful in setting this up, however. Careful setup will require two things, as follows:

- Proper configuration of multicast routers
- Proper choice of local MBone topology

Consider a company network "foo.com" that wants to create a private MBone within the bounds of its corporate network, as shown in figure 3.5.

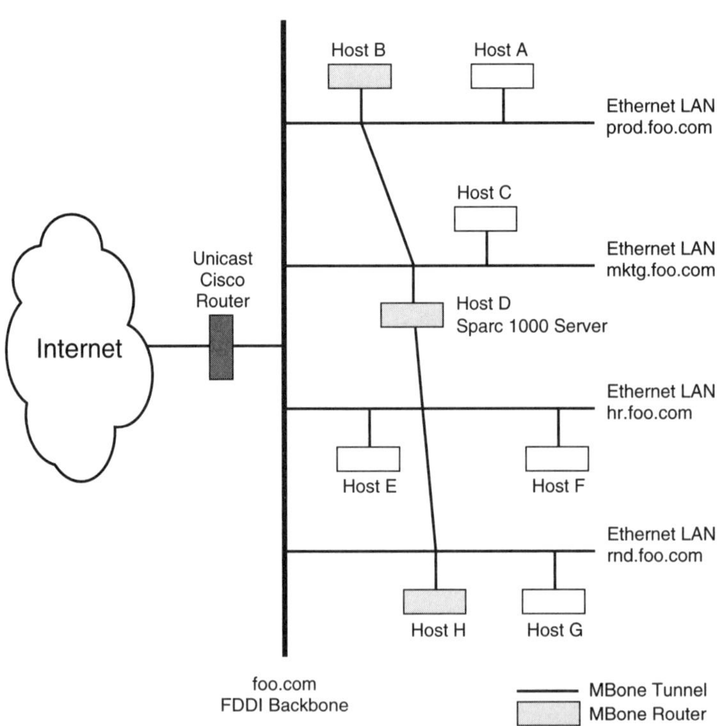

Figure 3.5

An example of a private MBone.

In figure 3.5, the network "foo.com" creates a private MBone that consists of subnets "rnd.foo.com," "mktg.foo.com," and "prod.foo.com." Here, Host D has been configured to provide two MBone tunnels—one to "rnd.foo.com" and the other to "prod.foo.com."

Note that there is no multicast data traffic on the subnet "hr.foo.com"; therefore, any host connected to that subnet cannot participate in any of the private MBone sessions.

Great care needs to be taken, however, in not connecting any of the MBone routers to the global MBone on the Internet. Connecting any of the MBone routers from inside "foo.com" to the outside global MBone routers will cause the private MBone traffic to flow outside "foo.com," as well as get an inflow of multicast traffic to "foo.com" from the outside.

Figure 3.5 shows only one of the topologies for interconnecting the mrouters. There could potentially be other ways to hook up the DVMRP tunnels to create the same private MBone. Note that, in the preceding example, Host D was chosen to be the main dedicated mrouter node to provide tunnels because this computing host will be the main routing hub. This host will replicate packets that arrived from the source and forward each copy to each of the connected tunnels.

Another more efficient method is to simply use native IP multicast routers (such as the Cisco-7000 product) for setting up local MBone and routing multicast data traffic. There is no longer a need for tunnels—the IP routers themselves understand multicast packets and, therefore, routing happens automatically. This method of routing is fast and efficient because processing overheads from tunneling no longer exist. Several organizations and IP service providers are already using this approach for multicast packet forwarding. Ultimately, all IP routers on the Internet will one day have native multicast packet routing, and tunnels will be completely eradicated from the MBone.

Traffic on the MBone

Traffic on the MBone consists of several types: the IGMP Queries/Reports, the mrouter DVMRP routing updates, and the application data. This section focuses on the application data because the rest of the traffic generated is very minimal (less than 1 Kbps). Application data consists of real-time audio data, video data, graphics, and text files.

Audio Data

The audio coding provided by the built-in audio hardware on most computer systems produces 64 Kbps PCM audio, which consumes 68–78 Kbps on the network with packet overhead. The audio applications that are available on the MBone implement software compression for reduced data rates as well:

- 36 Kbps *Adaptive Pulse Code Modulation* (ADPCM)
- 17 Kbps *General Special Mobile* (GSM)
- 9 Kbps *Linear Predictive Coding* (LPC)

Video Data

For the slow-frame-rate video (less than 30 fps) prevalent on the MBone, the compression, decompression, and display of the digital video frames are all done in software. The data rate that is typically generated is about 125–128 Kbps, with the maximum established by a bandwidth limit slider. Higher data rates may be used with a smaller TTL value within your local area network.

Graphics and Text Data

Graphics and text files are transmitted over the MBone with a much lower data rate. The bandwidth consumed is about 5–6 Kbps. A text chat, *WhiteBoard* (WB), or IMM applications generate data rates in that range as well. WB and IMM generate a higher peak data rate at the time a file is loaded and transmitted for sharing over the MBone. The rest of the interactions between users do not take up very much bandwidth—of the order of 1–2 Kbps or less.

Bandwidth and Traffic on the MBone

At the time of writing this book, the estimated guess is that a total bandwidth of 500 Kbps exists for the MBone at any given time. Thus, you can easily calculate how many simultaneous audio and video sessions are feasible within the given bandwidth constraints.

The traffic anticipated during the IETF multicasts is about 100–300 Kbps. Between IETF meetings, most of the time there is no audio or video traffic, though some of the amount of session/control traffic (a few Kbps or less) may be present. The peak level of experimental use might involve five simultaneous voice conversations at 64 Kbps each.

Note that the design bandwidth for a given media stream—for example, 72 Kbps for an audio session with one speaker—must be multiplied by the number of tunnels passing over any given link because each tunnel carries a separate copy of each packet. This is why the fanout of each mrouted node should be no more than eight or nine tunnels, and the topology should be designed so that at most one or two tunnels flow over any T1 (1.54 Mbps) link.

While most MBone nodes should connect with lines of at least T1 speed, it is possible to carry restricted traffic over slower speed lines as well. Each tunnel has an associated threshold against which the packet's IP TTL value is compared. The mrouted version 3.3+ also supports the <rate_limit> parameter that can be used to limit the maximum bandwidth use over a given tunnel.

Managing the MBone

Chapter 1, "The Internetwork Primer," described the MBone topology, which consists of mrouters, as a tree and a mesh (see fig. 1.12). Since the early days of the MBone, the topology has been laid out in such a way so as not to load any one individual with the responsibility of designing and managing the whole topology. It is not a centralized architecture—it is distributed. Network engineers from all around the world participate in managing and reengineering the topology. Internet Service Providers (ISPs), along with end users (typically system and network administrators), participate in all the topology management issues.

The intent is that when a new regional ISP or an organization wants to join the MBone, it will send a request on the appropriate MBone e-mail list. The participants at close nodes answer and cooperate in setting up the ends of the appropriate MBone tunnels. While adding new tunnels to the MBone, the fanout at each mrouter node has to be kept down, potentially less than eight or nine. To keep the fanout low, this may mean breaking an existing tunnel or inserting a new node, so all the involved sites have to work together to set up the tunnels.

To know which nodes are close requires knowledge of both the MBone logical map and the underlying physical network topology—for example, the physical *National Access Provider* (NAP) backbone topology map combined with the network service providers' own knowledge of their local topology.

Within a regional network, the network's own staff can independently manage the tunnel fanout hierarchy in conjunction with the end-user participants. New end-user networks should contact their ISPs directly, rather than the MBone list, to get connected. See Chapter 5, "MBone Resources," for a list of MBone service providers and how to contact them.

Internet Service Providers and the MBone

Chapter 1 described the growth of the MBone since its first deployment. This rapid and enormous growth could not have been possible without the active participation and the help of ISPs. ISPs provide MBone access as a value-added service to their customers for a relatively low cost, enabling their customers to participate in IETF audiocasts and other experiments in packet audio/video, and to gain experience with IP multicasting. In turn, ISPs and telephone companies benefit when customers request an upgrade in their IP service—for example, upgrading from a 56 Kbps IP service to a T1 service.

Each ISP participant in the MBone provides one or more IP multicast router to connect with tunnels to other major mrouter nodes of current ISPs, and also to customers. The multicast routers are typically separate from a network's production routers, unless they have upgraded their routing infrastructure with a hardware-based solution such as Cisco's PIM router, Alantec's DVMRP router, or Proteon's MOSPF router. In the meantime, most sites use Unix workstations to run the software mrouted program.

It is suggested that the workstations may be dedicated to the multicast routing function to avoid interference from other activities. Upgrading these mrouting workstations for newer and better operating system kernel patches and other software will not interrupt the functioning of regular services.

Because most MBone nodes (other than endpoints) will have at least eight tunnels, and each tunnel carries a separate (unicast) copy of each packet, it is also useful—though not required—to have multiple network interfaces on the workstation (also called multihomed hosts). This is so that it can be installed parallel to the unicast router for sites with configurations such as those found in figure 3.6.

Figure 3.6

A potential network configuration for multicast routing.

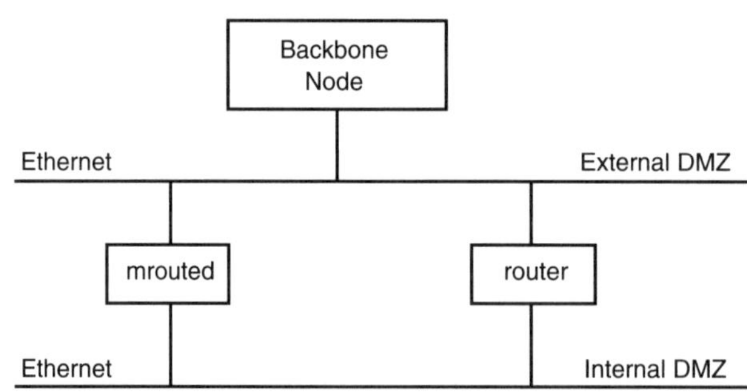

The *DeMilitarized Zone* (DMZ) Ethernets act as interface points between networks and machines controlled by different entities. This configuration allows the mrouted machine to connect with tunnels to other regional networks over the external DMZ and the physical backbone network, and also to connect with tunnels to the lower level mrouted machines over the internal DMZ, thereby splitting the load of the replicated packets. The mrouted machine would not do any unicast forwarding.

The end-user sites may participate with as little as one workstation. This workstation runs the packet audio and video software, and has a tunnel to the MBone service provider's node.

Administering the MBone

The person supporting an ISP's participation in the MBone should have the skills of an Internetwork engineer, but only a small percentage of that person's time is actually required. Two of the skill sets that an MBone administrator may be required to have include the following:

- Choosing a topology for multicast distribution within the provider's network
- Collecting and analyzing traffic flow characteristics when performance problems are identified

To set up and run an mrouted machine requires the know-how to build and install operating system kernels; some of these issues are discussed in Chapter 6, "System Administrator's Guide to the MBone." If the MBone administrator decides to use a hardware platform other than those that are currently supported in software, then it might also be helpful to have some software development and prototyping skills.

The MBone administrators for each network are strongly advised to subscribe to and read e-mail on the appropriate MBone mailing list, as discussed in Chapter 5. Using e-mail, the providers can respond to requests from new networks that want to join the MBone and are nearby (router hopwise) to coordinate the installation of new tunnel links. E-mail is used by both providers and customers to request, configure, and provide the MBone tunnel. When customers of the network provider make requests for their organizational network or end systems to be connected to the MBone, new tunnel links are added from the network provider's multicast routers to the end systems, unless the whole network runs hardware-based routing scheme.

Part of the ISP's resources for participating in the MBone should be committed for operations staff to manage and debug their part of the MBone topology. Such a staff would need to be aware of the role of the multicast routers and the nature of the multicast traffic. They would also need to be prepared to disable multicast forwarding if excessive traffic is found to be the cause of network trouble.

The potential problem is that any site hooked into the MBone could transmit packets that cover the entire MBone, especially when active receivers are very few and are not densely distributed. Therefore, if transmission became popular as a 24-hour chat line, then the available bandwidth could be overburdened. Most of these problems are going away gradually, however, as hardware routers optimized for scalable routing and better bandwidth management are being put into place.

As you can see, the overall management of the MBone is very distributed and loose, requiring almost everyone's participation. The end-user sites, the ISPs, and the *National Access Providers* (NSPs) are involved in administering the MBone. At the time of writing this book, measures are being taken to upgrade the MBone infrastructure in the form of deployment of native multicast routers, higher bandwidth, bandwidth management technologies, and real-time services on the Net. This will ease the burden of management, as well as spur growth in the MBone.

Chapter Summary

In this chapter, you have learned the underlying principles and technology behind the MBone. Class D addressing facilitates the idea of IP multicasting to achieve simultaneous multiparty and multihost group communications. Multicast routing is responsible for the notion of efficient, highly threaded models of IP-based multisite communication. Several algorithms for multicast routing are being practiced today on the MBone, namely DVMRP, MOSPF, and PIM. PIM seems to be the way of doing multicast routing in a scalable manner through the use of Sparse Mode and Dense Mode functionalities. It is still being deployed in the Internet marketplace, however, and test results have not come in yet. The outcome remains to be seen.

It is also quite clear that most of the Internet service providers are offering the MBone technology to their customer base as part of value-added service. In terms of network and bandwidth control technologies, however, easing the burden of active and fair management on the part of ISPs is an issue. Real-time service with proper quality of service and fair price are some of the issues that need to be addressed where the MBone is concerned. You will see more of these issues in subsequent chapters of this book.

p a r t

MBone Communications and Integration

chapter 4

MBone Multimedia Applications

In this chapter, you explore how the current MBone is being used for interactive multimedia over the Internet. The state-of-the-art MBone applications that are being used by millions of users worldwide are described. These applications are designed to scale for hundreds and thousands of simultaneous users, yet still are network friendly.

Currently, only a few classes of applications exist on the MBone—these are mainly focused at groupware or video-conferencing scenarios. *Visual Audio Tool* (VAT) and *Network Voice Terminal* (Nevot) enable a group of users to do voice conferencing, whereas *NetVideo* (NV), CU-SeeMe, VIC, and IVS facilitate video conferencing. Shared WhiteBoard and Shared Mosaic applications are also available for document conferencing. All of these applications use IP multicasting as the network transport to achieve scalability for supporting a large number of active senders and listeners.

MBone Rendezvous Applications

Before you can do audio, video, WhiteBoard, or Mosaic-based conferencing over the MBone, a multicast session needs to be allocated, reserved, and advertised. Once advertised by the creator of such a channel, each individual desktop needs to access such advertisements, and then be able to tune in and out of such sessions. Several such tools are described in the following sections.

Session Directory

The *Session Directory* (SD) tool is used by Internet MBone users to reserve and allocate media channels for distribution of media at one end, and then to surf and join these channels by different users at the other end. Thus, SD acts like the *TV Guide* of the MBone. The act of tuning into a channel is *receiver instantiated*—that is, the act of joining an ongoing media session is invoked by the receiver of the media; it is not invoked intrusively by the media source. Figure 4.1 displays a graphic snapshot of SD with its advertised channels.

SD was developed initially as a research prototype under the Unix and X Windows operating systems by Van Jacobson at the Lawrence Berkeley Labs, University of California, Berkeley. Consequently, it is available only for computing platforms such as SunOS, IRIX, HP-UX, DEC-OSFV2, and Intel PCs running Linux and FreeBSD operating systems.

To use SD, just type **sd &** (i.e., this will run it in the background). You should see an X window with two panes and some buttons across the bottom, as shown in figure 4.1. If you leave SD running, the top pane should slowly fill with session (or channel) names. SD announces these sessions quite infrequently, but they are announced periodically over a well-known multicast address and a UDP port (224.2.2.2 and 4000). The amount of data that is transmitted in these announcements is quite minuscule, and therefore doesn't take up any significant amount of the available network bandwidth.

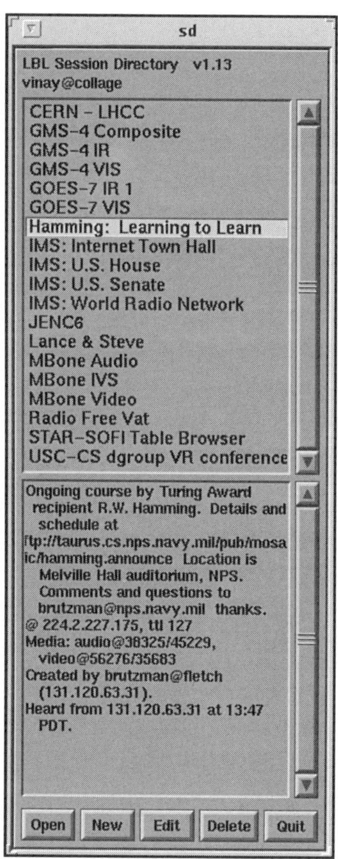

Figure 4.1

The Session Directory tool showing its list of advertised channels.

If you click on a session name, information about the session will appear in the bottom pane. If you double-click on the name (or click on the Open button), SD will start up the appropriate media tools for the session selected.

Creating a New Session

If you want to create a new session (or channel), click on the New button. A dialog box will pop up, as shown in figure 4.2.

Fill out all the entries in the dialog box to describe the nature of your session. This includes selecting one or more media types, such as voice, video, and/or WhiteBoard. Media subtypes can also be selected based on need; such subtypes include pcm, adpcm, gsm, and lpc for voice, and NV, VIC, and IVS for video. If you do not select these media subtypes before clicking on "Create," however, then SD will pick the default values for the new session.

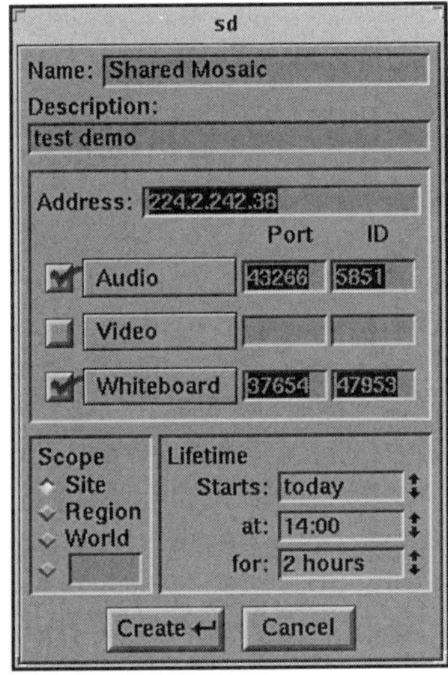

Figure 4.2

The sd dialog box for creating, reserving, and advertising a new session.

The box marked "Scope" enables you to select the scope (multicast TTL—TTL is defined in a later section of this chapter) of the session. There are four categories to choose from, as follows:

- Site is a TTL of 16
- Region is a TTL of 32
- World is a TTL of 127
- Other

The last option will let you choose a custom TTL value of your choice—type in a number between 0 and 255. So, for example, if you decide to create a session for people within your organization located on the same LAN, then you will choose the Site TTL of 16. If some of the participants are located outside your subnet, then you will have to choose a higher TTL range, such as the Region TTL of 32.

After entering all necessary information in the sd dialog box, clicking on "Create" will create a new multicast media session. By default, SD chooses a unique, nonconflicting multicast address, port, and conference ID for the session.

VAT, NV, and WB should be in your shell search path in order to make SD instantiate audio, video, and WhiteBoard media tools.

SD is a very sophisticated software package in terms of how it allocates and manages the MBone multicast address space. It is designed to be flexible and extensible via the sd.tcl configuration file that is bundled in the distribution. SD enables what no other Internet tool has made possible—that is, a fully distributed Internet *TV Guide* for creating, reserving, and managing global MBone-based multimedia channels or sessions. More details on the use of this tool are available in the README file that is bundled with the software distribution.

Multimedia Conference Control

Multimedia Conference Control (MMCC) is another rendezvous software that allows multiple Internet sites to participate in interactive multimedia sessions, either on a person-to-person basis or in a multiparty scenario. The rendezvous scheme in MMCC is more intrusive in nature, as compared to the SD tool. The rendezvous call will interrupt the called party either by popping up a window, or ringing the speaker of the called party's workstation. MMCC uses voice, video, and other groupware applications to explicitly invite other participants into a multimedia interaction over the MBone.

To start up MMCC, just type **mmcc &**. MMCC must be running on a remote user's workstation in order to rendezvous with that user. The MMCC window may be closed to place it out of view when it is not in use. Any incoming requests will automatically reopen the window.

Configuring MMCC

MMCC can be configured to start up with a database of remote user aliases and addresses. By default, mmcc looks for the file ".mmccrc" in your home directory. The -f option may be used to specify a different user configuration file (see the man page for further details). Each line in the config file includes an alias for a user, the user's login ID, and the user's workstation host name or host address. The port field is optional, and by default has a value of 5050; a port may be specified as a decimal or hexadecimal value (e.g., 0x13BA). Create your own "~/.mmccrc" file as you begin to acquire remote users' addresses.

There is a public user configuration file that is maintained in the file ftp.isi.edu:confctrl/.mmccrc that will enable you to bootstrap with other mmcc users. To add (or delete) yourself to the public registry, send an e-mail message to <schooler@cs.caltech.edu> with the Subject field "Add to .mmccrc" ("Delete from .mmccrc"). The content of the message should be in .mmccrc format. For example:

"Dr. J."	jirving	192.100.56.2
"Nomad"	collage	animation.newrid.com

Creating a New Session

A new session can be instantiated using the MMCC tool by following the six-step process described next. First, however, you'll want to refer to figure 4.3, where you'll find a graphical illustration of the MMCC window.

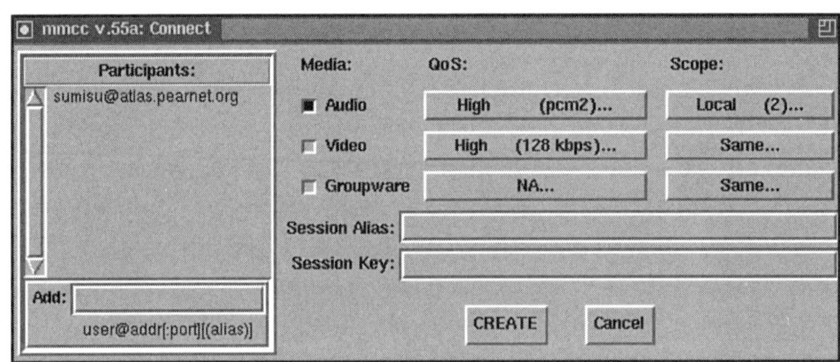

Figure 4.3

A sample MMCC window.

The six-step process is as follows:

1. **Start.** As shown in figure 4.3, click on the "Connect" button in the main MMCC window.
2. **Session name.** Type a session name in the "Session Alias" field. If this field is left blank, the name of the session is automatically generated and is based on the session initiator's alias.
3. **Security and privacy.** If you want your session to be secure and private, then you can specify a session encryption key by typing a password string in the "Key" field. Only the users who have access to the same password will be allowed to join the session; others will be denied access.
4. **Choose a participant(s).** Under the "Participants" list, use the left mouse button to click on the aliases of any remote users who should be included in the session. Repeated clicking on the same user's name toggles the selection.
5. **Add new participants, if necessary.** To include a user not in your user configuration file, click left, then type in the "Add" field at the bottom of the "Participants" list.

The fields correspond to the fields of the user configuration file, such as the "user" and "addr" fields. If unspecified, "alias" defaults to "user@addr" or "user@addr:port." When the entry is complete, simply press Enter to enter it in the participant list and select it. There currently is no automated way to save new participant entries in the user configuration file.

6. **Select media types and subtypes.** Under the "Media" list, select the media to be included in the interactive session. Currently, the choices include:

Media	*Audio*	*Video*	*Groupware*
Programs:	VAT	NV	WB
QoS:	Low: gsm	56 Kbps	
	Medium: idvi	92 Kbps	
	High: pcm2	128 Kbps	

Note that the Audio, Video, and Groupware media types have been mapped to the MBone tools, such as VAT, NV, and WB. The choice of TTL will be decided by the session creator. After choosing the appropriate parameters for the session, you must click on the CREATE button to initiate the session, or on "Cancel" to cancel the request.

Accepting an Invitation

When a remote user requests your participation in a conference, your MMCC window will open itself and pop to the front of your screen. By default, it double-beeps to get your attention. You can configure MMCC to play a sound file to get your attention, however, by placing a sound file called ".mmcc.au" in your home directory, or by passing MMCC the play option on the command line.

Session Status

Session status may be observed by clicking on the "View Status" button on the main MMCC panel. Status includes the list of session participants, as well as the details associated with the session—the session alias, session key, media included, TTLs, and QoS choices. The status information is dynamically updated, and disappears automatically when the session is closed.

Disconnecting a Session

Use the Disconnect button on the main MMCC panel to leave an ongoing session. The conference is terminated when fewer than two sites are left in a session.

Exiting MMCC

Type **q**, **Q**, or **^C** anywhere in the main MMCC panel to quit the program. Alternatively, those of you running OpenWindows may use the "Quit" option in the frame menu to exit. If the Connect panel is open, it will have to be closed before the program itself will close.

The MMCC software was developed at the Information Science Institute by Eve Schooler. It is now available in binary form, and is available for most Unix platforms for free via anonymous FTP. See Appendix A, "MBone Resources on the Internet," for details.

Multimedia Phone Service

Multimedia Phone (Mmphone) is a rendezvous tool that differs from others—it makes use of *Multipurpose Mail Extensions* (MIME) multimedia e-mail as the transport method. Mmphone is a way of doing a rendezvous session in a very flexible nonintrusive manner. It is flexible because the same service can also be set up as an intrusive service, where the called party is interrupted by the invitation. Currently, Mmphone is set up as a Web-based service that makes use of *Simple Mail Transfer Protocol* (SMTP) and MIME-based e-mail and the MBone tools such as VAT, NV, and WB. The Mmphone Web service is accessible via Web browsers such as Mosaic and Netscape, and looks like that shown in figure 4.4.

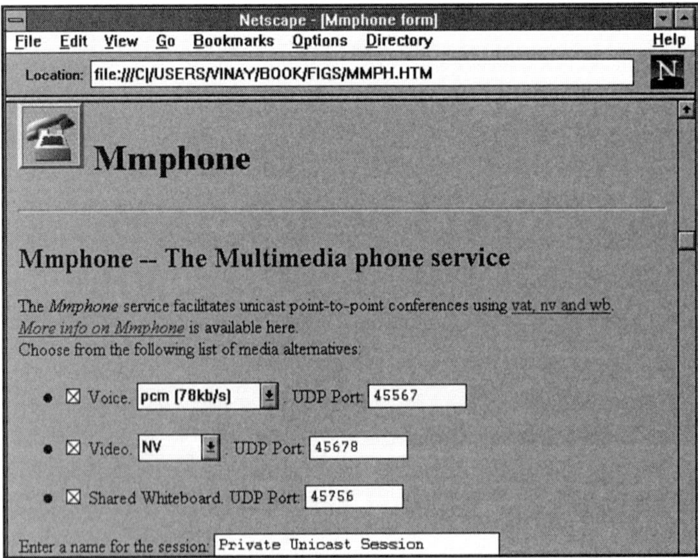

Figure 4.4

The Mmphone Web service page.

Using this service, you can set up unicast point-to-point multimedia sessions. Thus, Mmphone acts as an e-mail-based multimedia ring for MBone-based audio and video conferences. The main uses of Mmphone include the following:

- To initiate VAT, NV, and WB in a user-friendly manner for unicast conferences
- To notify the remote party of your intent to do a real-time multimedia interaction, without being too intrusive
- To facilitate a remote site to connect to an already instantiated unicast multimedia session

The service sends a MIME e-mail message to the remote party. This special multimedia invitation message is quietly delivered to the called party's electronic mailbox. The remote party at the other end will see this e-mail message with the following "Subject:" heading:

Subject: Invitation to join an Mmphone conference call

On reading the message, the called party can decide whether to accept the invitation. If the called party decides to accept, then the multimedia invitation message will spawn off the appropriate media tools (VAT, NV, and WB) and connect to the caller's session.

An important difference between Mmphone and other rendezvous tools is that Mmphone does not require the called party to have access to the same Mmphone software. A public domain MIME parser software such as "metamail" will be able to process the Mmphone invitation messages as well.

Mmphone was developed by the author while he worked at Enterprise Integration Technologies, and was also presented at the IETF in Danvers, Massachusetts, April 1995. See Appendix A for details on how and where to access this service and the software.

Real-Time Video Delivery

Real-time video is becoming very important in our lives, especially in the electronic world of computers and fast networks. Video has traditionally been used for local multimedia—that is, created, presented, and stored on the same stand-alone computer. With fast networks like the MBone, live video is no longer stand-alone. Video images are captured and authored on one machine, then delivered over the MBone to remote computers for display and archival. From this explanation, it is easy to see that we are moving into the age of digital networked video.

A simple setup for today's multimedia desktop connected to the MBone is illustrated in figure 4.5.

Figure 4.5

A video workstation setup for the MBone.

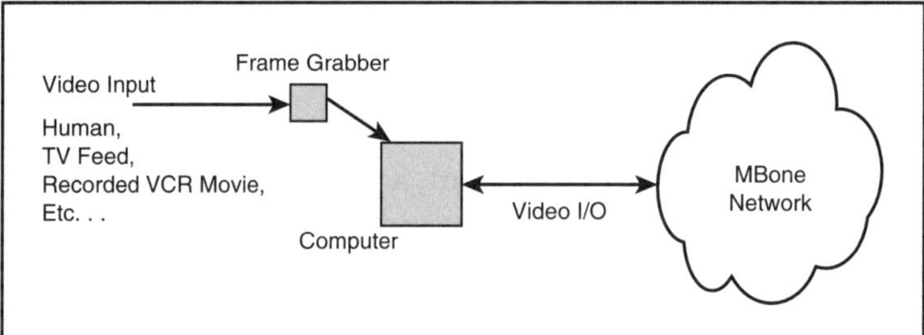

In this section, you will learn about some of the near real-time video delivery software prototypes such as CU-SeeMe, NV, VIC and IVS. Some of these software exploit the power of the MBone; others are in the process of transitioning. Regardless of their status, the bottom line is that these software all enable real-time live video delivery on a large scale.

CU-SeeMe

CU-SeeMe provides a one-to-one live video connection, or by use of a reflector, a one-to-many, several-to-several, or several-to-many conference depending on user needs and hardware capabilities. It displays 4-bit grayscale video windows at 160x120 pixels or at double that diameter, and also includes audio. So as far as the author knows, CU-SeeMe was the first software available for personal computers that supports real-time multiparty videoconferencing on the Internet. It does not use the MBone, however. There are no multicasting functionalities built into CU-SeeMe yet, partly because of the lack of support for IP multicasting in the Mac operating system kernel. Figure 4.6 shows an illustration of CU-SeeMe.

Receiving CU-SeeMe video requires only a personal computer with a screen capable of displaying grayscale images and a connection to the Internet—no additional hardware or software is needed. Sending CU-SeeMe video requires the same tools as when receiving, plus a camera and video capture hardware such as a SuperMac VideoSpigot board. At this time, CU-SeeMe also runs on Intel PCs under MS-Windows. With CU-SeeMe, each participant can decide to be a sender, receiver, or both.

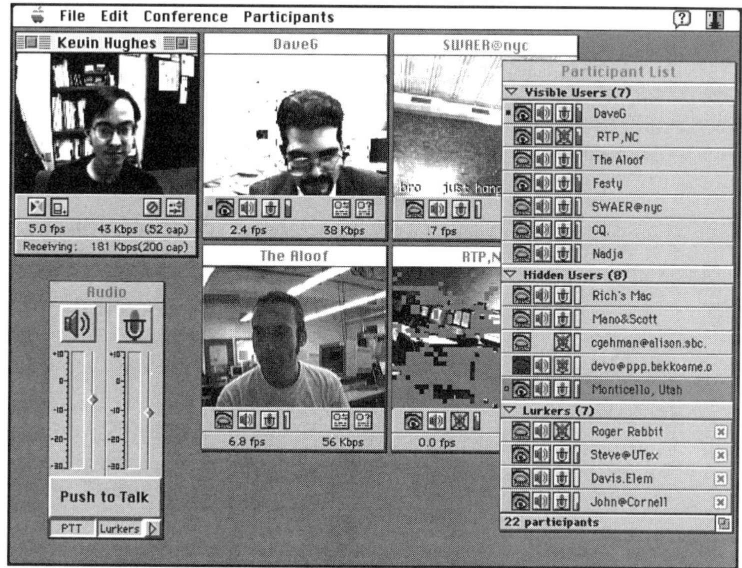

Figure 4.6

A graphical view of CU-SeeMe.

The Development of CU-SeeMe

At Cornell University in 1993, the CU-SeeMe grassroots development strategy was realized as interest in CU-SeeMe grew rapidly with training and user support from the *New York State Educational Research Network* (NYSERNet). NYSERNet spread the word among Internet users by providing one of the first public reflectors, encouraging users to try out this technology.

Because CU-SeeMe uses simple but efficient video frame-differencing and compression algorithms, it opens networked videoconferencing capability to users of lower-cost desktop computers, and thus enables broader participation in desktop video technology. Once the live video is captured at the sending end via a frame grabber card, it is encoded in a compression format called CUSM. At the receiving end, the CUSM-encoded video is decompressed and displayed on the user's Mac or PC desktop (see fig. 4.7).

CU-SeeMe Reflectors for Multiparty Conferencing

CU-SeeMe essentially is a point-to-point communication software—that is, it enables only two people sitting on two remote computers to do videoconferencing. There is a great demand, however, for multiparty videoconferencing in scenarios such as school lectures, meetings, workshops, seminars, and so on. In addition, the MacOS TCP/IP suite did not support IP multicasting in the kernel. Thus, the idea of reflectors was invented.

Figure 4.7

The CUSM encoding and decoding process in CU-SeeMe.

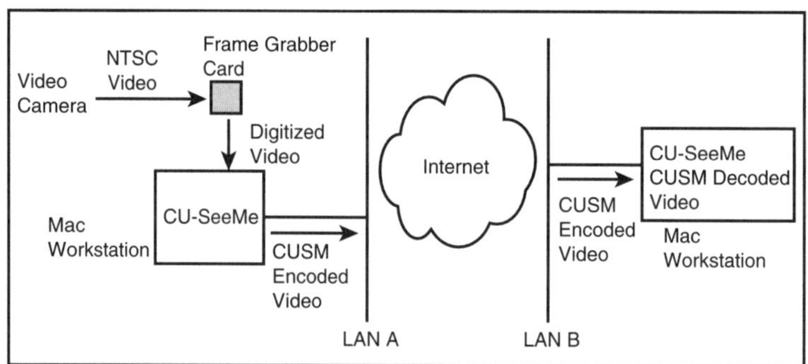

CU-SeeMe reflectors now provide the capability to send IP multicast video streams, but no functionality to receive them. In concept, a reflector configuration looks like the illustration in figure 4.8.

Figure 4.8

A CU-SeeMe reflector configuration.

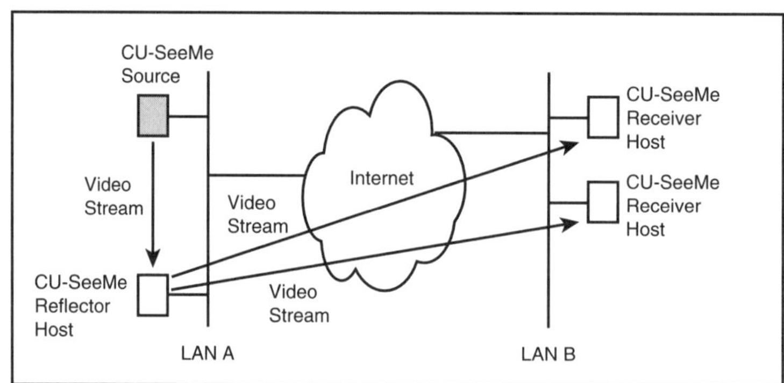

As shown in figure 4.8, the CU-SeeMe reflector takes one CU-SeeMe video input stream from the remote CU-SeeMe video source, and makes multiple copies of the video stream to send them out to remote CU-SeeMe receivers on LAN B. The output video streams can either be multiple IP unicast streams or just one IP multicast stream.

Note that the CU-SeeMe reflector runs only on Unix machines, and configuring the reflector is no easy task. It is not very user-friendly and not very well documented. Ask your system administrator to configure and install it. A sample configuration file looks like this:

```
MOTD
        CU-SeeMe NEW REFLECTOR 4.00B1
        Welcome to the CU-SeeMe Reflector. Please do not transmit more than 80 Kbps
➥of video.
```

```
CONF-MGR 204.192.155.24
CONF-ID 0
CAP 80 1
MAX-PARTICIPANTS 15
MAX-SENDERS 10
ADMIT 192.101.58.18
DENY 101.23.45.127
```

The preceding configuration file will allow a reflector to run on a Unix machine with an IP address of 204.192.155.24. A conference ID of 0 means anyone can join into the reflector and send or receive CU-SeeMe video. This reflector is also configured for a maximum participants of 15 sites, but only 10 sites are allowed to send CU-SeeMe video at any given time. Each participant is allowed to send only video at data rates of 80 Kbps or less. The ADMIT parameter refers to a specific IP host (here 192.101.58.18) on the Net being allowed to connect to the reflector. The DENY parameter does the opposite—it denies specific IP hosts (here 101.23.45.127) to connect to the reflector. There are numerous other specifiers that can be used to customize the reflector. Please access and look at the file included in Appendix A. Once the configuration file is properly customized, you can start the reflector just by typing **reflect &**.

Following these instructions will enable you to configure CU-SeeMe correctly. Now any CU-SeeMe participant can connect to a video session simply by specifying the IP address of the host running the reflector, and a conference ID of 0.

Reflector Etiquette

In consideration for those who operate reflectors, please observe the following practices specified by the developers and maintainers of the reflector software:

- **Do** e-mail the contact person for each reflector to clarify your use of the reflector, how you are planning to use the connection, and for (approximately) how long.
- **Don't** stay connected for extended periods of time (hours) unless invited to do so. "Hanging out" is something to do on your own reflector, but not on remote reflectors.
- **Don't** leave a video transmission going with a still image—or worse—with a message crawling. It uses bandwidth on the Net and capacity on the reflector.
- **Don't** play a VCR tape. CU-SeeMe opens up ready access to live video. Canned video typically uses more bandwidth, as well as conveys any old information better transmitted in another medium.
- **Don't** set your Max Kbps (cap) above 100 Kbps. Preferably, just use the defaults.

Currently, CU-SeeMe conferences are open to viewing by anyone who connects with an active reflector. Anyone who hangs out on an active reflector can see anyone who tunes in to that reflector—reflector software repeats all streams of a conference to all receivers.

NetVideo

NetVideo (NV) is one of the most popular real-time video delivery and access software for the MBone. Like CU-SeeMe, it enables multiple parties to send and receive live video images across the Internet MBone. The NV program can be seen in figure 4.9.

NV uses a new video compression algorithm, which is designed specifically for network video to achieve low data rates and high frame rates. NV also uses the *Real-Time Protocol, version 1* (RTPv1) as the underlying application transport for transmitting and receiving video streams. NV software can also decode CU-SeeMe video streams encoded in the CUSM format. NV comes prebundled with video drivers for most frame grabber cards for live NTSC video I/O.

Like most other MBone tools, NV can also be used in both unicast point-to-point and multiparty scenarios.

In figure 4.9, the Hamming lecture series was being received live from the NPS Labs in Monterey, California, over the MBone. The figure reveals that NV is tuned into the multicast address 224.2.227.175 and port 56276. All the viewers and one sender have to tune into the same multicast address and port in order to communicate via multicast mode.

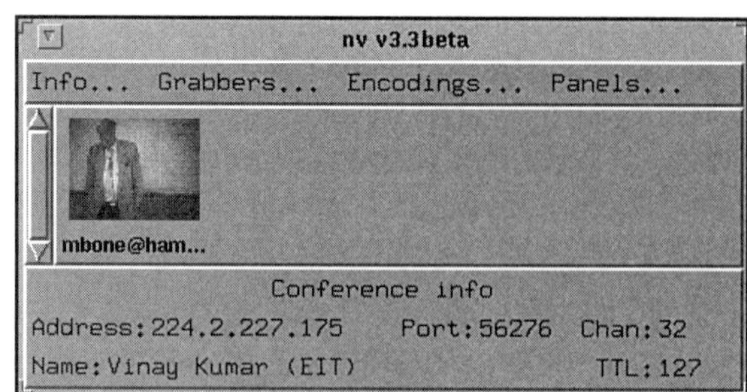

Figure 4.9

An NV video display with one video source over the MBone.

If you clicked on the video icon shown in figure 4.9, you would get a bigger video window (one-half size NTSC, 320x240) frame. See figure 4.10 for a representation of this scenario.

Figure 4.10

A one-half size NTSC, 320x240 pixel, NV video window.

Using NV

In order to describe the use of NV, consider a scenario where Bob and Alice want to do a desktop conferencing session using live NV video. Assume that Bob is sitting in front of a machine named collage with an IP address 192.101.59.18, and Alice sits in front of a host named zip with an IP address 36.100.24.16.

Thus, Bob types the following command on his terminal:

nv zip 4545 &
or
nv 36.100.24.16 4545 &

And Alice types:

nv collage 4545 &
or
nv 192.101.59.18 4545 &

where 4545 is the mutually agreed-upon unreserved UDP port. This agreement is done out of band, sometimes using the rendezvous tools like Mmphone, MMCC, and SD.

Let's now assume that both Bob and Alice want to invite two more individuals (Mike and Barb) to the next desktop conferencing session. The best way to do this will be via the Session Directory tool, but in essence the following will happen.

Each individual will type the following command on his or her host to join a live video session:

nv 224.2.24.45 4545 -ttl 16 &

where 224.2.24.45, 4545, and 16 are the reserved, mutually agreed-upon multicast address, IP port, and TTL values respectively. Obviously, the TTL value is chosen based on the number of IP router hops each party is away from each other.

Additional NV Considerations

The NV video has been found to produce smooth video texture, even during fast motion of the object. Typically, you get frame rates of about three to five frames/sec (1/2 NTSC) when compression and decompression is done in software on a SunSPARC 2 level machine using a cheap Sun VideoPix frame grabber board. The video grabber card is not required for receiving video images, however.

The NV user interface seems to lack a few helpful things that may be beneficial to new users, such as a warning about the data rate slider bar. Typically, new users move the slider bar to the rightmost corner and increase the data rate to almost 1 Mbps without realizing its effects on the MBone. You should not, in any circumstance, increase the slider bar more than 128 Kbps when sending the video over the MBone. You may, however, increase the data rate when sending video over the local area Net by keeping the TTL value to 16 or less. Again, consult your system and network administrator before doing this.

NV was developed by Ron Frederick at Xerox PARC. It is available only for the Unix platform running X Windows. See details in Appendix A on how to access the software.

VideoConference

VideoConference (VIC) was designed with a flexible and extensible architecture to support heterogeneous environments and configurations. In high bandwidth settings, for example, multimegabit full-motion JPEG streams can be sourced using hardware-assisted compression, while over lower bandwidth environments like the Internet, aggressive low bit-rate coding can be carried out in software.

VIC is based on version 2 of the *Real-Time Transport Protocol* (RTP), which provides basic real-time media communication support. RTP is an application-level protocol and is implemented entirely within VIC—you need no special system enhancements to run RTP. Although VIC can be run point-to-point using standard unicast IP addresses, it is primarily intended as a multiparty conferencing application.

To make use of the conferencing capabilities, your system must support IP multicast and, ideally, your network should be connected to the MBone. VIC is backward compatible with RTPv1 and can interoperate with both NV (v3.3) and IVS (v3.3).

Using VIC

In order to understand the use of the VIC tool, let's go back to the example you have been following thus far—that is, Bob and Alice. If both Bob and Alice are hooked up to the MBone, then both could type the following command to watch the live video lecture series of Dr. Hamming from Monterey, California (see fig. 4.11):

vic -A nv 224.2.227.175/56276/127 &

Figure 4.11

Live MBone video, as seen through VIC in NV-compatibility mode.

As usual, the viewers and receivers of the video need to somehow know the multicast address, port number, and TTL for the session to tune into. This problem is resolved out of band—for example, via the rendezvous tools like the SD tool. The size of the video window can be controlled by each viewer by clicking on the Size button, shown in figure 4.11.

Consider Lance and Steve, who are conducting a workshop remotely for thousands of people on the MBone (see fig. 4.12). Let's also assume that the workshop is coming live over the reserved multicast address 224.2.193.162, port number 58664, and with a TTL of 127. As a result, both Lance and Steve, along with all potential receivers of this video, will type the following on their hosts:

vic 224.2.193.162/58664/127 &

Note that by typing the preceding command, VIC is being used in its native mode. The native mode implies use of H.261 as the video compression/decompression scheme, and RTPv2 as the application transport mechanism.

Lance and Steve could also limit access to their seminar either by using a smaller TTL value or by encrypting the H.261 video feed with a password. Only the people who have access to the password would thus be allowed to tune into the seminar. The encryption is built into the VIC software and is based on a 40-bit, fast, exportable version of DES standard. Most other VIC options are available by clicking on the Menu button. Figure 4.13 shows all the available features.

Figure 4.12

Lance and Steve giving a remote interactive seminar using VIC over the MBone.

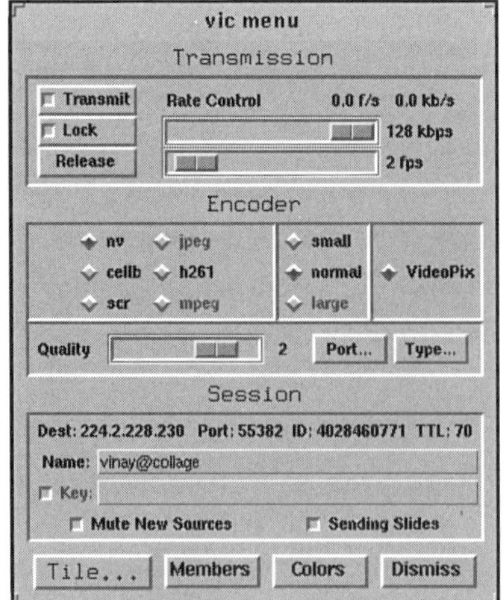

Figure 4.13

Menu options in the VIC tool.

Features of VIC

Features unique to VIC include a robust H.261 video encoder and voice-activated video switching. The robust-H.261 encoder combines the advantages of NV's block-based conditional replenishment scheme (i.e., robustness to loss) with those of H.261 (i.e., higher compression gain and compatibility with hardware codecs). For a fixed bit rate, the H.261 coder achieves frame rates typically 2–4 times that of the NV coding format.

In voice-activated switching, a viewing window can be configured to "follow the speaker." Using cues from the audio conferencing VAT tool, VIC will switch the viewing window to whichever source is speaking. This helps in scenarios where you have multiple video windows displayed on your computer console. VIC also has a nice built-in rate control mechanism that is tied to the TTL used for the transmission for a video session. As a result, VIC prevents accidental use of high data rate video feeds with large TTL values.

VIC was developed by Steve McCanne and Van Jacobson at the University of California, Berkeley, at the Lawrence Berkeley Labs. VIC is available on most Unix platforms, including Intel PCs running Linux and BSD/386, and most video frame grabbers. See Appendix A for details on how to download this software using FTP.

INRIA Videoconferencing System

INRIA Videoconferencing System (IVS) is a software system to transmit audio and video data over the Internet using a standard workstation (see fig. 4.14). It was developed by Thierry Turletti at INRIA—a computer science research agency in France. IVS software is quite popular with European MBone users, especially in several European research projects, such as the MICE project in England and the RODEO project in France. IVS includes PCM and ADPCM audio *codecs* (short for coder and decoder), as well as a H.261 video codec. Both audio and video codecs are software codecs. Hence, only minimal hardware upgrades are required to a machine commonly found on the user's desktop, namely a video camera and a frame grabber for those users who need to transmit video.

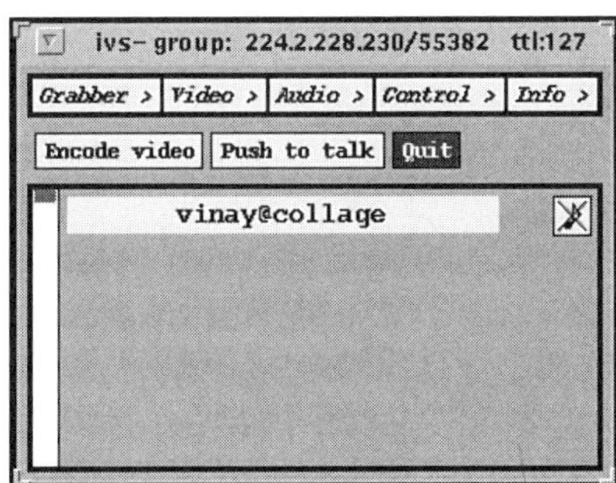

Figure 4.14

An IVS window showing the user interface components.

IVS enables you to use standard Internet technology to transmit video and audio data. This is achieved by implementing PCM and ADPCM audio codecs and a software version of an H.261 codec. A PCM audio codec, for example, can encode raw digital audio stream into PCM compressed audio, as well as decode a PCM compressed audio back to raw digital audio. The same case exists with video codecs.

The H.261 software video codec of IVS uses standard UDP/IP datagrams encapsulated inside RTPv1. IVS also includes an error control scheme based on RTP to handle packet losses in the Internet. Since version 3.3, IVS includes a feedback rate control scheme that adapts the image coding process, and hence the output rate of the coder, depending on network conditions. The feedback information is periodic loss-rate measurements sent back from decoders to the coder.

IVS software also comes bundled with an extensive suite of utilities for recording an ongoing IVS conference, playing back a recorded IVS conference, a rendezvous utility for inviting new IVS participants for a unicast conference, and a gateway utility to make IVS work with your organizational firewalls. See Appendix A for details on how and where to download the software using FTP.

Real-Time Audio Delivery

When only two remote users are involved in a voice conference, it is also called the unicast mode or point-to-point mode (see fig. 4.15). Unicast mode does not require IP multicast extensions; therefore, most MBone tools work on any host that is connected to the Internet, with or without IP multicast capability.

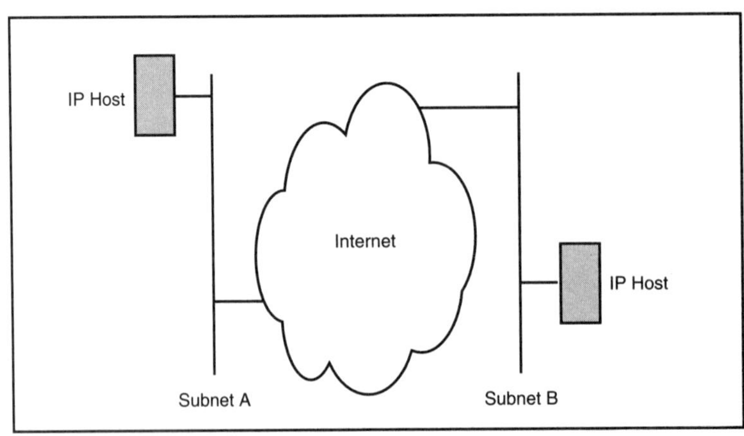

Figure 4.15

Unicast mode communication between two IP hosts across Internet WAN.

In a multiparty scenario that involves more than two users on multiple sites that may or may not be on the same subnet, it is called the multicast mode (see fig. 4.16). Multicast mode requires that each participating host operating system support IP multicast extensions.

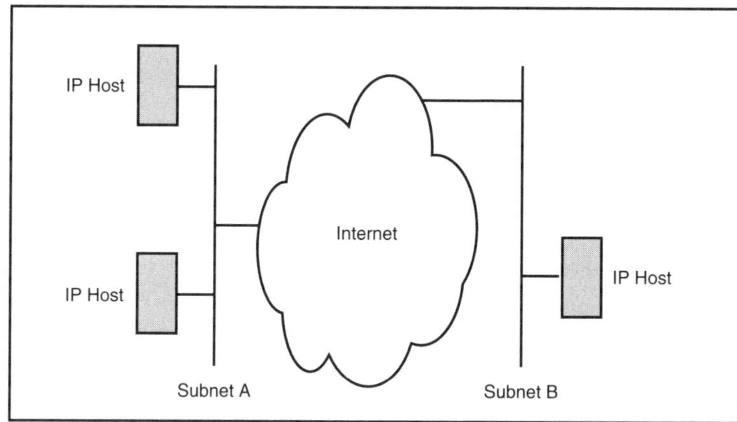

Figure 4.16

Multicast mode communication between IP multicast-enabled hosts over the MBone.

In this section, you will explore various uses of all the real-time MBone audio delivery tools, such as MAVEN, VAT, and Nevot.

MAVEN

MAVEN is a Macintosh-based real-time audio delivery software for the Internet. It was developed by Charley Kline at the University of Illinois, Urbana-Champaign. MAVEN facilitates multiple remote hosts to share "real-time" interactive audio sessions. The design of MAVEN is quite analogous to that of CU-SeeMe software in the sense that it only supports point-to-point audio interactions. MAVEN by itself does not work over the MBone, partially because of lack of support for IP multicast extensions in the MacOS.

MAVEN is compatible, however, to Unix-based VAT audio software—it follows the same audio packet format as the VAT protocol, discussed next.

Visual Audio Tool

The *Visual Audio Tool* (VAT) was developed by Lawrence Berkeley Labs at the University of California, Berkeley, by Van Jacobson and Steve McCanne. VAT enables two or more Internet hosts to participate in voice-based conferencing, much like a telephone (see fig. 4.17).

Currently VAT is supported on most Unix platforms, including Intel-PCs running Linux and FreeBSD operating systems. VAT does not run on Windows or Macintosh machines yet. The software only requires sound I/O devices, such as the microphone, a speaker, and an audio hardware board.

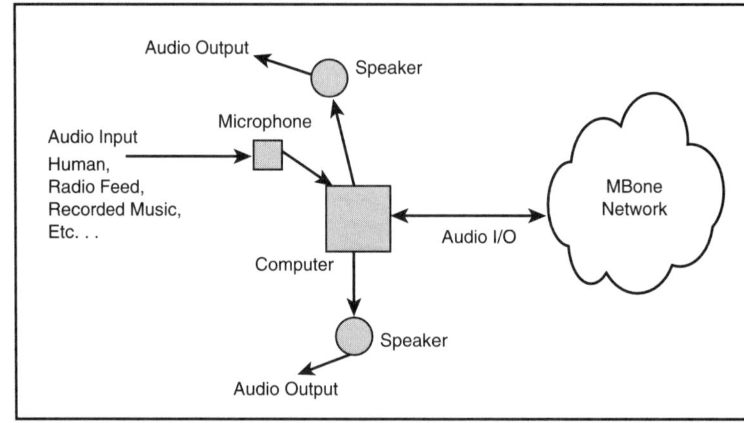

Figure 4.17

A multimedia workstation configuration for doing real-time audio delivery and access over the MBone.

The VAT Experience

Doing an interactive real-time voice session with VAT is quite different and, in this author's opinion, much better than traditional telephone-based voice conferencing. VAT enables you to see who is talking in the session, and therefore avoid confusion about the identity of the speaker. VAT displays the identity of all the participants in the session and highlights the speaker identity. Speaker and listener ID consists of login_name and Internet host name by default, but this can be changed to a custom ID chosen by the user. An example of an ID is as follows:

vinay@viper
or
vinay@prince.mbone.com
or
Vinay Kumar

Another major advantage of such a digital desktop voice conferencing system is the easy archival and integration of such conferences into your personal or corporate information systems. Most personal and corporate information systems exist in digital form on computers, thus allowing easy integration of VAT-style interactive voice media to your information system. This suddenly increases the usability and usefulness of such interactive media. Such integration is much harder to achieve using existing analog telephone systems and digital computer systems.

The VAT Scenario

Let us now consider a scenario where Bob, sitting on an Internet host named prince, wants to talk to Alice on host collage. This is how both Bob and Alice will use VAT for a real-time voice conversation. On host prince, Bob types **vat collage/4545 &**. On host collage, Alice types **vat prince/4545 &**.

Note that both Alice and Bob use the same nonreserved IP port number, here 4545. Agreement of a common port number is done out-of-band. Other tools, such as Mmphone and Session Directory, help to achieve this, and were described earlier in this chapter.

Once both Alice and Bob are connected, they will see each other's names in the VAT window (see fig. 4.18).

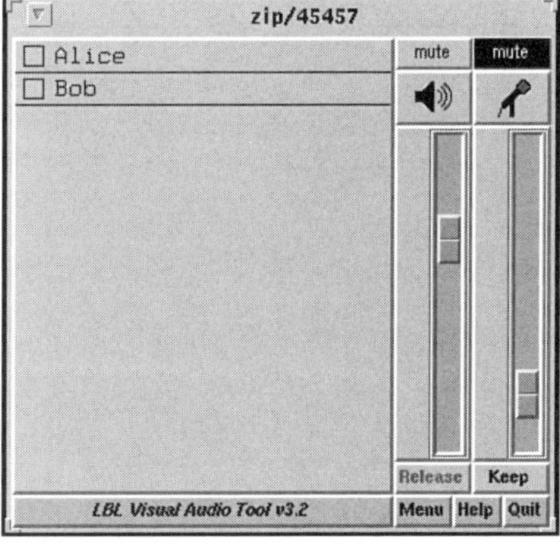

Figure 4.18

A unicast VAT session showing Bob's and Alice's connection.

Both Bob and Alice can now take turns speaking to each other by activating the microphone icon in the VAT window and speaking into the microphone. The microphone should be shut off when you finish speaking, much like a walkie-talkie. Hands-free full-duplex operation is possible if both Bob and Alice use a headset instead of speakers for voice output. If you choose the headset option for voice output, then make sure you select the option by clicking on the speaker icon in the VAT window.

In the multicast mode shown in figure 4.19, two or more users on remote machines can connect to each other via a common multicast address and port number.

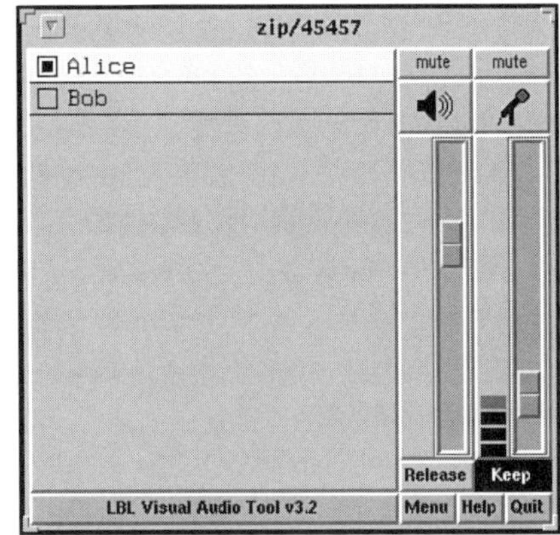

Figure 4.19

A VAT session showing Alice as the speaker and Bob as the listener.

In figure 4.20, three participants will see each other's names listed as shown. Each participant will type the following command on his or her respective workstation to connect to each other:

vat -t 127 224.2.44.55/4545 &

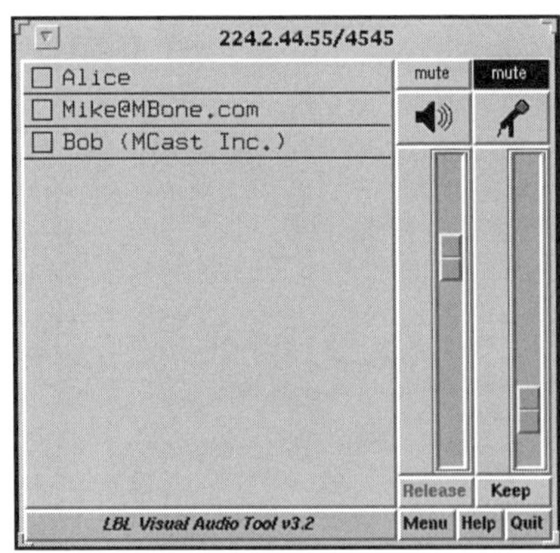

Figure 4.20

A multicast VAT session over the MBone.

How did we agree on the preceding multicast address, port numbers, and TTL? The ideal way to do this is via the Session Directory tool, described earlier in the chapter.

A typical voice interactive session over the MBone may look like that shown in figure 4.21.

As shown in the figure, there are about 20 listeners from around the world listening to the MBone channel called the "IMS: World Radio Network." There is one news source feed highlighted as "World Radio Network."

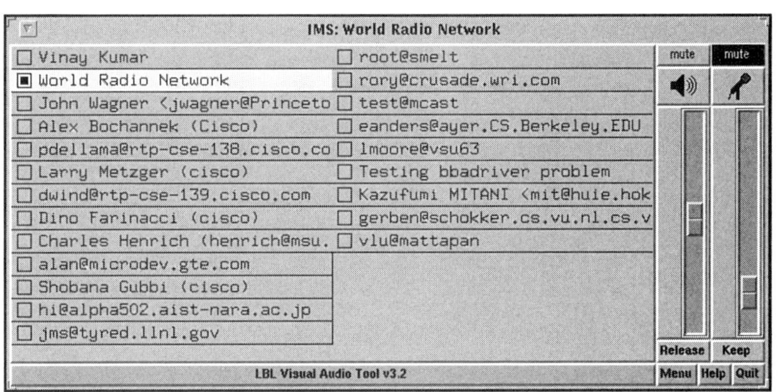

Figure 4.21

The World Radio Network on the MBone, as seen in VAT.

More VAT Advantages

Clicking on the menu button at the bottom right corner of the VAT window will pop up the window shown in figure 4.22.

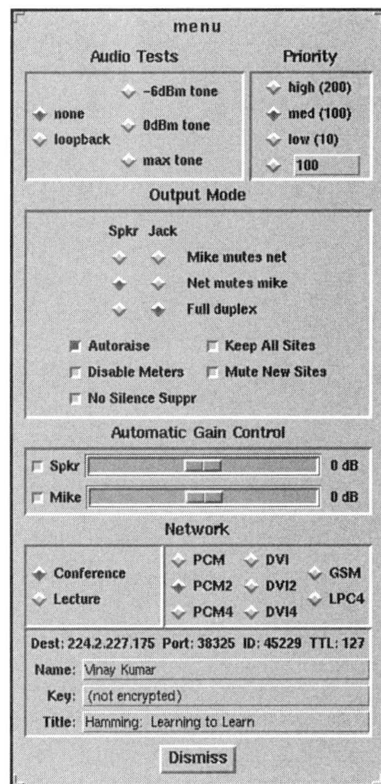

Figure 4.22

The VAT menu options for customized audio I/O.

This window enables you to set special custom parameters for the conference. VAT currently supports various audio encoders and decoders at different data rates, as follows:

- PCM (Pulse Code Modulation): 78 Kbps 8-bit mu-law encoded 8 KHz
- IDVI (Intel DVI, Adaptive PCM): 46 Kbps
- GSM (General Special Mobile): 17 Kbps
- LPC4 (Linear Predictive Coder): 9 Kbps

The VAT menu options window enables you to select the appropriate voice encoding scheme, personal ID string, name for the session, privacy/secrecy option with password, and more.

Encryption and privacy is enabled by entering an arbitrary string in the key box. This string is the previously agreed upon encryption key for the conference—note that key distribution should be done by mechanisms totally separate from VAT.

Most of these options are described in great detail in the manual pages that are bundled with the software distribution.

Network Voice Terminal

Network Voice Terminal (Nevot) is another software that allows multiple sites to conduct interactive real-time audio-based interactions on the MBone. Nevot was developed by Henning Schulzrinne while he was at the University of Massachusetts, and at AT&T Bell Laboratories. Henning continues to add enhancements to Nevot while he works at Fokus, GMD.

Nevot is a Unix and X Windows-based nifty voice conferencing tool with a clean modular software design and lots of functionality. The user interface is quite intuitive and is quite fun to use. Nevot can be used in conjunction with the SD tool, as well as with stand-alone software for point-to-point or IP multicast-based multipoint conversations.

In order to use Nevot on your desktop, you need to make sure that a small program called PMM is already running on your computer—Nevot will not start without PMM running. PMM is included in the Nevot software distribution and can be started by typing the following:

```
pmm &
```

Nevot can be started by simply typing:

nevot &

Once started, you will see a small window pop up in the top right corner of your screen (see fig. 4.23). Clicking on the Join button enables you to input either a unicast IP address of a remote host or an IP multicast address for an MBone session. The settings for the session can be changed at any time by clicking on the Settings button. This will pop up the window shown in figure 4.24. This window is also called the Configure Session window.

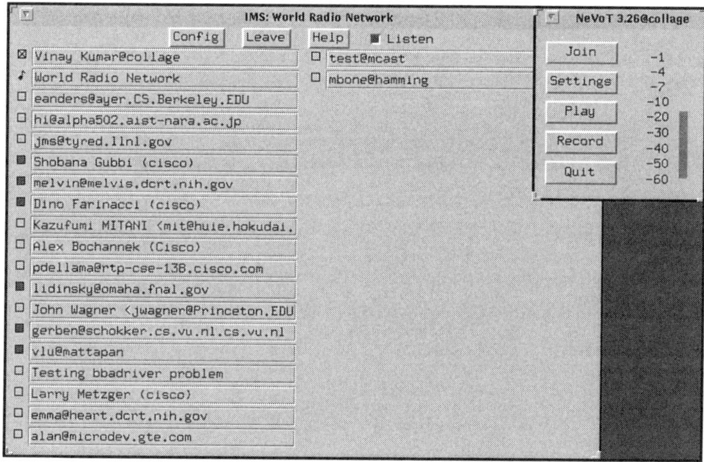

Figure 4.23

Nevot tuned into the World Radio Network on the MBone.

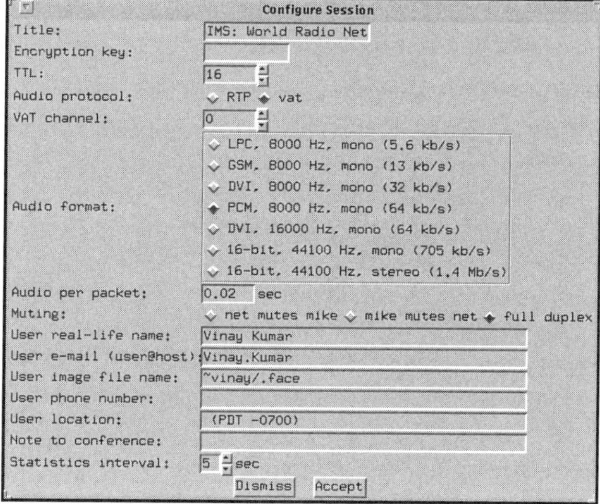

Figure 4.24

The Nevot Configure Session dialog box.

The Configure Session window enables you to set TTL values for the session and choose an appropriate voice encoding scheme, much like in the VAT tool. Notice that the Audio Protocol option is selected by default as VAT. It can, however, be changed to RTP if you prefer. This is done in order to make Nevot backward compatible with the more popular VAT tool. Notice that by choosing VAT protocol as the option, you can have voice communication with remote individuals who may or may not be using the Nevot tool. Eventually, VAT will support RTP as the transport mechanism, in which case you would want to select RTP as the voice transport protocol.

Most other advanced options are well-documented in the manual pages that are bundled with the software. The distribution also comes with Web-accessible HTML-based help pages. See Appendix A for more details on how and where to access this software.

Real-Time Document Feeds

The traditional notion people have about the MBone is that it works only over high bandwidth connections, and that IP multicasting can only be used for fast, high-speed networks. In this chapter, however, you will take a tour that will prove such notions to be pure myth. IP multicasting is quite independent of the speed of the underlying network. On the MBone today, several less bandwidth-intensive experimental prototypes are being used. The software packages include Shared Mosaic, WhiteBoard, IMM (a client/server image distribution package), and others. All of these software packages will be discussed in this section.

Shared Mosaic

Shared Mosaic is an extension to NCSA's WWW browser XMosaic. Using Shared Mosaic, you can conduct *What You See is What I See* (WYSWIS) collaborations. People sitting on desktops can take each other on a tour of sorts in the Web space. It is a loosely controlled session; therefore, anyone can drive on the Web highway and give others a tour according to their particular likes and dislikes.

Shared Mosaic was developed by the author for the Unix and X Windows platforms.

Shared Mosaic Features

On unicast IP machines, you can conduct a meeting in point-to-point mode using Shared Mosaic. Any of the two parties can share an URL simultaneously by clicking on a hyperlink, by opening an URL via hotlists, and so forth.

On IP multicast machines, two or more Shared Mosaic clients, each running on remote desktops, can share a set of URLs at the same time. In wide area situations, each site is required to be connected to the MBone. A Shared Mosaic session is loosely controlled, meaning there is no explicit control over who (individual or site) controls the session. Almost anyone in the session can decide to share an URL at any given time; therefore, problems relating to synchronization of views may arise. The author suggests that informal session control via live audio and video MBone tools, such as VAT and NV, be used during a Shared Mosaic session.

In figure 4.25, the extra session window shows the list of participants in the live session. The window also highlights the names of individuals who initiate sharing—that is, transmit URLs for others to look at. The tool also comes with support for text-based chat. The textual chat messages are also shared over the same MBone channel.

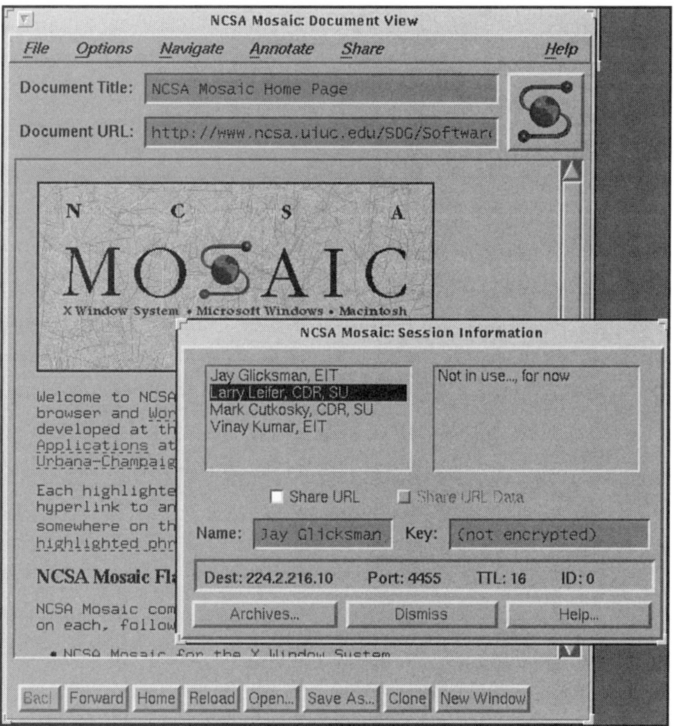

Figure 4.25

A Web-based document being shared over the MBone via the Shared Mosaic software.

It should be noted that this form of real-time collaboration over the Web does not require any special servers to be installed at each Web site. All the necessary functionality is embedded inside the Mosaic client, and almost any URL that is accessible via a standard Web client can now be shared. A newer and more feature-filled version of the same software is expected in the future, including support for Windows and MacOS clients. See Appendix A for more details on how and where to access the software.

WhiteBoard

WhiteBoard (WB) was developed at Lawrence Berkeley Labs of the University of California, Berkeley, by Van Jacobson and Steve McCanne. WB is a another good example of an MBone application that works over the Internet in low bandwidth conditions. The data rate achieved by WB is far less than those via audio and video delivery applications.

WB allows one or more sites to share documents in real-time—it is a document-sharing application that operates both in unicast and multicast modes. Documents can either be in Adobe PostScript format or plain ASCII text.

Once a user decides to load and share a document, the document also gets transmitted to other participants in the session. The session control is loose and informal, meaning that almost anyone can control the sharing session. In this case, control means that the user is allowed to type text, draw graphics, and make freehand annotations. In order to prevent miscreants from interfering in an ongoing sharing session, however, special features have been built into WB, such as the capability to start a session in Lecture mode. This mode will not prevent miscreants from joining an ongoing session, but will ensure that none of their interactions are transmitted to other participants and therefore will keep them from being visible. Other special features like DES-based encryption also help in keeping unwanted users away from a session.

Note that WB is not a drawing tool—it is a simple canvas for sharing and brainstorming via simple text, graphics, and annotations (see fig. 4.26). This figure shows that WB is tuned into an ongoing WB MBone session on multicast address 224.2.193.162, IP port number 47198, and an IP TTL value of 127. WB could be instantiated either via the SD tool or on the command line by typing the following:

```
wb 224.2.193.162/47198/127 &
```

When run, the WB program will also pop up an additional secondary window that displays the session information, such as who else is listening to the session, who is interacting with the session, and who has quit the session, as well as other network-related parameters (see fig. 4.27).

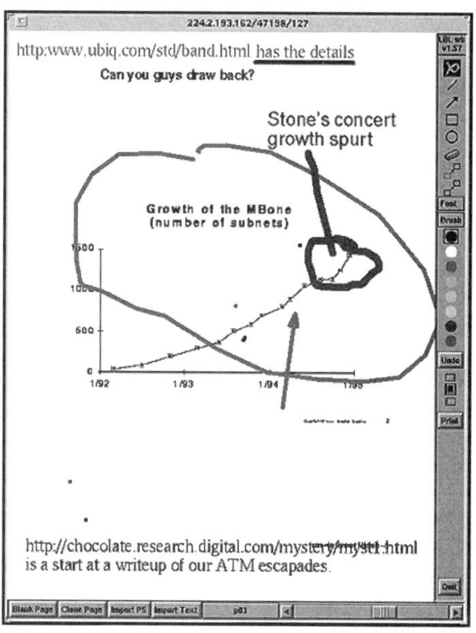

Figure 4.26

Document-based free-form interactions on the MBone via the WB software.

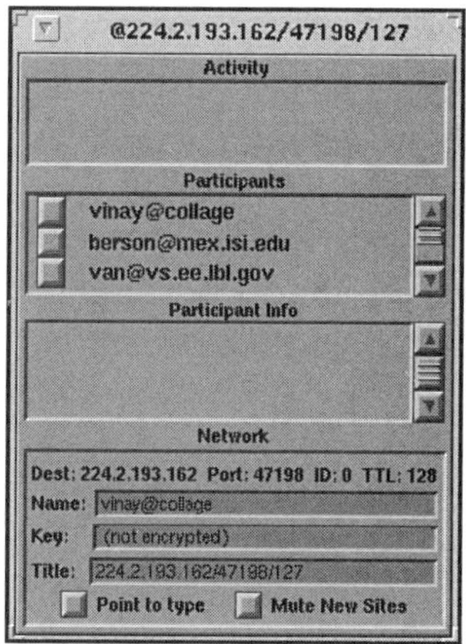

Figure 4.27

A WB session window showing a list of participants.

The WB program does not use the RTP protocol for its application transport needs. It does, however, use its own similar protocol called the WB protocol [1] (see bibliography). WB is available today for free use in binary form for most Unix workstations. See Appendix A for more details on where and how to access the software.

IMM

IMM software differs from other software packages in the fact that for most users it is a view-only software. It is built as a client/server package—the server multicasts graphic images over the MBone, and the client receives and displays these images on a user's desktop screen.

IMM is used today as a low bandwidth-consuming application for the MBone. One site at the University of Hawaii regularly multicasts graphic images of weather data and funny cartoon clips over the MBone. The transmissions from the server are quite infrequent—approximately one image every ten minutes. Therefore, the bandwidth consumption is comparatively much lower than other software packages. The client software accepts these transmissions and displays the image in the background of your X Windows system.

The server software runs only on Unix machines, whereas the client software runs under the Unix and X Windows systems. IMM can also be launched from the SD tool or via the command line.

IMM was developed at the University of Hawaii by Winston Dang. See Appendix A for more details on where and how to access this software package.

MBone Etiquette

There are no formal procedures for scheduling the use of the MBone—at least, not yet. Management of the bandwidth is a cooperative procedure that depends upon the good behavior of the participants. Typically, discussion of the use of the MBone happens on the rem-conf@es.net mailing list. Some discussion also occurs on the MBone mailing list, though the MBone list is intended more for MBone engineering issues.

Many events are announced by a message to rem-conf. An announcement might ask for expressions of interest or objections in order to determine whether the event would be appropriate to broadcast. Then, events are usually advertised using SD so that interested recipients can easily join. There is also a Web site that manages the reservation issues and the agenda for each upcoming MBone event (see Appendix A). So far, there has not been any significant objection to the content of scheduled events. Generally, the events have been on topics "of interest to the networking community" because that is what constitutes the demographics of the MBone users. These demographics are changing fast, however.

It is fortunate that, thus far, conflicts have not presented a big problem. With a wider user community, for example, conflicts might arise between conferences for physicists and historians occurring at the same time. One week, for example, the NASA Shuttle transmission ran all week, but they cut back the rate of the video during a couple of other events by request. It's clear that as the MBone grows and the capability to transmit becomes available at more events, more conflicts will occur. So far, MBone users have been reluctant to establish more formal procedures (either to be the czar or to submit to one).

Most MBone events are expected to be advertised via the rem-conf mailing list, the MBone agenda reservation Web site (see Appendix A), and the SD tool. In the SD advertisements, creators of a session can add additional instructions or pointers to instructions via an URL as a way to inform users (viewers and listeners). These instructions usually describe the do's and don'ts regarding an MBone transmission. Generally, people do adhere to such etiquette. The World Radio Network newscast, for example, requires that listeners cannot interrupt the audio news feed, and users follow the etiquette like good netizens. Nothing prevents them from being a miscreant by sending their own audio feed on the same channel, however. This is obviously undesirable behavior.

Eventually, multicast service and real-time service will be integrated into the whole network, and usage will be managed by cost.

Chapter Summary

In this chapter, you have clearly seen some of the applications and uses of the MBone. The common perception is that the MBone consists of just audio and video. It is quite clear now, however, that the MBone is more than just these elements—it is text and graphics as well. VAT, Nevot, VIC, and NV make up the primary audio and video tools, whereas Shared Mosaic, WB, and IMM make up the text and graphics capabilities of the MBone. Like most other new tools and technologies, some of the MBone tools are not available today on the popular DOS, Windows, and MacOS-based platforms. This scenario is happening, however—by the time this book is published, you will probably see a few of the MBone tools available for the popular platforms.

chapter 5

MBone Resources

This chapter discusses the online and non-online MBone-related information resources that are currently available. Information presented here pertains to some of the MBone-related management platforms, such as the IETF, along with several mailing lists on the Internet, different kinds of online resources for MBone software, *Frequently Asked Questions* (FAQs), and several popular MBone events that have been organized in the past. In particular, you will look at some of the high-speed multimedia networking projects that use the MBone or IP multicast technologies, and are happening worldwide.

Online Information

It seems appropriate to start by briefly describing some of the volunteer efforts made by individuals and organizations worldwide to put together online information about the MBone and related technologies. Several such sites exist today on the Internet, and are discussed in the following sections.

MBone Home Pages

The MBone Home Pages are the Web sites on the Internet that serve specific localized or global MBone-related information. These will be covered in more detail in the next section.

Global MBone Home Page

The Global MBone Home Page site was developed by the author, and, according to reader feedback, was the first of its kind to describe aspects of the MBone in a simple, intuitive, easy-to-read form (see fig. 5.1). This Web site is available via the following:

```
http://www.mbone.com/techinfo/
```

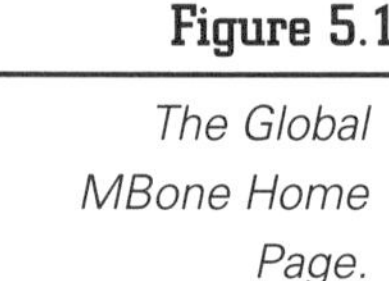

Figure 5.1

The Global MBone Home Page.

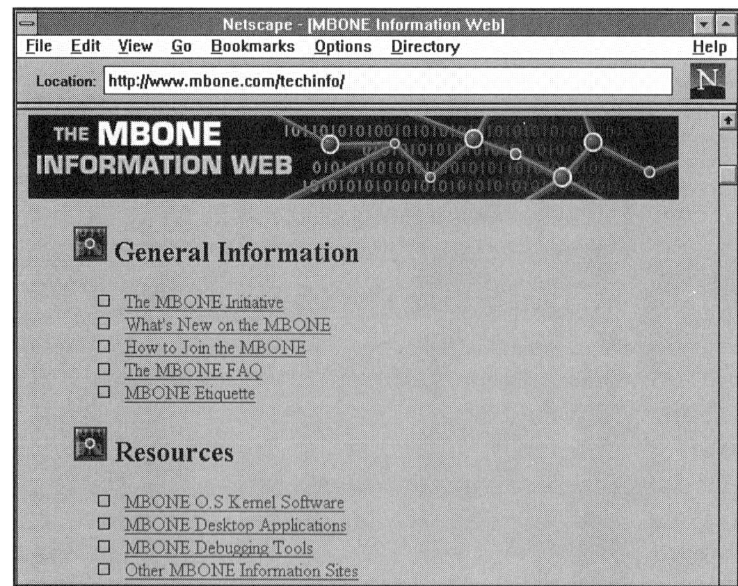

This site also takes you to all other major MBone information and software sites, so it acts as a good starting point.

JIPS MBone Page

Originally developed and managed by Piete Brooks in England, the JIPS MBone Page has information on several MBone tools, FAQs, and services. Because this site is not in the U.S., and the U.S.–England Internet link is not high speed (T1—1.54 Mbps), Web access from IP hosts located within the U.S. thus can be slow. This JIPS MBone site is accessible, however, via the following:

```
http://www.cl.cam.ac.uk/mbone/
```

This page describes several MBone administration and debugging tools and where they can be downloaded from. The information content on this site is very useful; however, the presentation needs some attention by the site's author as the page is currently difficult to read.

AT&T MBone Page

The AT&T MBone Page has a very nicely organized version of the MBone FAQ—that is, Frequently Asked Questions about the MBone. This site explains common questions about the MBone with answers in a hyperlinked fashion. The site was originally developed by Dave Kristol and Henning Schulzrinne of AT&T, with assistance from Steve Casner of ISI. This site can be reached at the following:

```
http://www.research.att.com/mbone-faq.html
```

Most of the contents of this page are highly technical in nature, but provide a good look at the MBone technology. Some of the information may already be obsolete, however, so handle with care.

NPS MBone Page

The *Naval PostGraduate School* (NPS—Monterey, California) MBone information page has a useful set of pointers to MBone information. This page is accessible via a Web client at the following:

```
http://taurus.cs.nps.navy.mil/pub/mosaic/mbone.html
```

This site also has a well-written paper by Don Brutzman and Mike Macedonia that describes NPS's use of and experience with various MBone applications on the Internet.

Geneva University MBone Page

Geneva University operates a Web site describing the MBone through a paper written by Jean Bunn. The paper takes you through various aspects of the MBone, such as IP multicast addressing, MBone applications, and several good references for further reading. This site can be reached via the following:

```
http://www.unige.ch/seinf/mbone.html
```

DEC-SRC MBone Page

Digital Equipment Corporation, Systems Research Center (often referred to as DEC-SRC) has an MBone Page with up-to-date information on various MBone tools available for the DEC-Alpha workstations. This site was created by and is maintained by Lance Berc. The site is available at the following:

```
http://chocolate.pa.dec.com:80/mbone/
```

VideoMaker/CableLabs Page

Audio and video enthusiasts can find interesting information about the Internet in relation to audio and video media at the Videomaker Magazine Web site and CableLabs Web site. These Web servers are available at the following:

```
http://videomaker.com/
```

or

```
http://videomaker.com/edit/distrib/
```

and

```
http://www.cablelabs.com/
```

or

```
http://www.cablelabs.com/NR/main_page.html
```

Internet Mailing Lists

There are several Internet mailing lists that handle the MBone and related activities. Much like any other Internet mailing lists, almost anyone is welcome to join these mailing lists—they are moderated by one or more individuals, and each list has a specific agenda or task.

MBone Engineering Mailing List

For all MBone engineering-related issues, the following mailing lists have been put into place. You can subscribe to any of these mailing lists by putting the word "subscribe" in the subject header and the body of the e-mail message. Table 5.1 displays mailing lists that fit into this category.

Table 5.1

Mailing Lists for MBone Engineering Issues

Country	Mailing List Address
Australia	mbone-oz-request@internode.com.au
Canada	canet-mbone-request@canet.ca
Japan	mbone-jp-request@wide.ad.jp
Korea	mbone-korea-request@cosmos.kaist.ac.kr
Singapore	mbone-sg-request@lincoln.technet.sg
United Kingdom	mbone-uk-request@cs.ucl.ac.uk
Europe	mbone-eu-op-request@ripe.net
Europe	mbone-eu-request@sics.se
North America	mbone-na-request@isi.edu
Global	mbone-request@isi.edu

The focus of the preceding MBone mailing lists is to look at the reengineering issues facing the MBone—that is, how to improve multicast routing, determining which IP host/router is misbehaving and how to fix it, new IP multicast kernel software releases, bug-reporting and fixes, and so forth.

Remote Conferencing Mailing List

Another Internet list for all MBone and non-MBone-based multimedia remote conferencing issues is the rem-conf mailing list. If you are interested, you can subscribe to the following:

```
rem-conf-request@es.net
```

This list is used to discuss various MBone multimedia networking applications, their appropriate use, problems, solutions to problems, new conferencing applications, and so forth. Much of the traffic is also related to announcing reservations of agenda for upcoming events on the MBone.

Conference Control Mailing List

Related to rem-conf issues is another mailing list called the *conference control* (confctrl) list. The confctrl list members look at various technology issues relating to the control of a conference, such as how a desktop multimedia conference should be initiated, how a remote participant should be invited, or, once the participants join, how the conference should be moderated. For all conference control-related issues, subscribe to the following:

```
confctrl-request@isi.edu
```

Radio Channel Mailing List

There is a fairly popular, regularly scheduled event on the MBone called the *Radio Free Vat* (RFV). This event is also advertised in the session directory (SD) tool. The RFV channel is essentially a music distribution and access channel, but also enables almost anyone on the MBone to volunteer to be a music disc jockey. The disc jockeys then play the music of their choice for other listeners on the MBone. RFV multicasts music live every Friday evenings, 11:00 p.m. U.S. Pacific Standard Time. In order to reserve a time slot to become a disc jockey on the RFV channel, an electronic mailing list has been created. You can subscribe to this list by sending mail to the following:

```
vat-radio-request@elxr.jpl.nasa.gov
```

Mailing List Archives

The discussions on various Internet mailing lists are sometimes archived on one or more Internet sites so that users can go back to them for review. Some of the MBone-related mailing lists are also archived; these are available at the following:

```
ftp://ftp.isi.edu/mbone/mbone.mail.*
```

The rem-conf mailing list archives are available at the following:

```
ftp://nic.es.net/pub/mailing-lists/mail-archive/rem-conf
```

The confctrl mailing list archives are available at the following:

```
ftp://ftp.isi.edu/confctrl/confctrl.mail
```

IETF Groups

Chapter 1 briefly covered the meaning of the *Internet Engineering Task Force* (IETF) and its goals. The IETF also has played an important role in the engineering and standardization of various MBone technology and deployment issues. This section discusses some of the IETF groups that are currently very active in spearheading the MBone and related activities on the Internet. The IETF itself has a Web server that contains information about the IETF as an organization, its activities, and various standards document archives. This Web site is accessible via a Web client at the following:

```
http://www.ietf.reston.va.us/home.html
```

AVT Working Group

The *Audio Video Transport* (AVT) Working Group was responsible for all the real-time audio and video communication issues on the MBone. The issues relate to design of real-time multimedia collaboration tools, networking protocols, and their use and deployment on the MBone. The end product of this working group was an Internet standards draft called the *Real-Time Protocol* (RTP), which has since been published as an Internet RFC (see Chapter 6, "System Administrator's Guide to the MBone," for details). This draft is available at the following:

```
ftp://ds.internic.net/internet-drafts/draft-ietf-avt-rtp-07.txt
```

or

```
ftp://ietf.cnri.reston.va.us/internet-drafts/draft-ietf-avt-rtp-07.txt
```

Further information on the AVT Working Group charter is accessible at the following:

```
http://www.ietf.cnri.reston.va.us/html.charters/avt-charter.html
```

MMU.S.IC Working Group

The demand for Internet multimedia teleconferencing has arrived as evidenced by the explosive growth of the MBone. A multimedia teleconference session involves multiple media (such as audio, video, documents, text, and graphics), multiple Internet hosts, and multiple participants. Such a complex environment thus requires flexible session coordination, advertisement, and management protocols. The *Multiparty MUltimedia SessIon Control* (MMU.S.IC) Working Group is chartered to design and specify these protocols to perform these functions, and to facilitate interoperability between different teleconferencing implementations. A detailed description of the official charter for this working group is available at:

```
ftp://ftp.isi.edu/confctrl/charter
```

or

```
http://www.ietf.cnri.reston.va.us/html.charters/mmusic- charter.html
```

IDMR Working Group

The routing of multicast data traffic via existing inter-domain multicast routing protocols (such as DVMRP, MOSPF) is not scalable to a large Internetwork containing very large numbers of active wide-area multicast groups. The purpose of the *Inter-Domain Multicast Routing* (IDMR) Working Group, therefore, is to discuss proposed inter-domain multicast routing protocols, and put forward one protocol (or a hybrid of several) as a proposed standard. More information on the official charter of this working group is available at the following:

```
http://www.ietf.reston.va.us/html.charters/idmr-charter.html
```

IDMR-related issues are also discussed via Internet mailing lists; subscribe to the following:

```
idmr-request@cs.ucl.ac.uk
```

INT-SERV Working Group

In the *Integrated Services* (INT-SERV) Working Group, "Integrated Services" refers to the capability of the Internet infrastructure to seamlessly transport audio, video, real-time, and other data traffic. The experiments on the Internet (such as the MBone) suggest that the current Internet service model needs to be expanded to deliver such complex multimedia services in a fair fashion. The purpose of this working group is to specify this enhanced service model, and then to define and standardize certain interfaces and requirements necessary to implement the new service model.

The INT-SERV Working Group charter is quite closely related to the RSVP Working Group, and several participants cross-participate in both discussions. The official charter for this working group is available at:

```
http://www.ietf.reston.va.us/html.charters/intserv-charter.html
```

General discussions in this topic happen on the INT-SERV mailing list (`int-serv@isi.edu`). Subscribe to the following:

```
int-serv-request@isi.edu
```

The archives of these e-mail discussions are available at the following:

```
ftp://ftp.isi.edu/int-serv/int-serv.mail
```

RSVP Working Group

RSVP is the *Resource reSerVation setup Protocol* for the Internet. The primary purpose of this working group is to evolve the RSVP specification and to introduce it into the Internet standards track. The working group also serves as a meeting place and forum for those developing and experimenting with RSVP implementations. As the name suggests, RSVP enables flexible reservation of network resources (bandwidth, for example) on demand for a certain guaranteed *Quality of Service* (QoS). RSVP also focuses on use of IP multicast for efficient distribution of Internet data traffic. The RSVP Working Group has made much progress since its inception a year ago. Today, one can anonymous FTP sample implementations of RSVP for SunOS operating system kernels and IP routers. Many MBone users and service providers have already incorporated such RSVP features. Most operating systems and IP router vendors are now busy porting and embedding RSVP features into their products.

The official charter for this working group is available at:

```
http://www.ietf.reston.va.us/html.charters/rsvp-charter.html
```

General discussions usually happen over the rsvp@isi.edu mailing list. Subscribe to the following:

```
rsvp-request@isi.edu
```

The archives of these RSVP discussions are available at:

```
ftp://ftp.isi.edu/rsvp/rsvp.mail
```

MBone Service Providers

In Chapter 6, you will see that in order to participate in the global MBone, you have to set up your local subnet for MBone services. One small but crucial step involves requesting a tunnel from your local IP service provider—that is, if you are using a DVMRP-based software multicast router, which in all probability you are. The request for an MBone tunnel follows a small and simple hierarchy (see fig. 5.2).

As shown in figure 5.2, the end users must follow the hierarchy for requesting an MBone service. Today, not all IP service providers support MBone services, although most of them do. Table 5.2 contains a list of the MBone service providers.

Figure 5.2

An MBone tunnel request hierarchy.

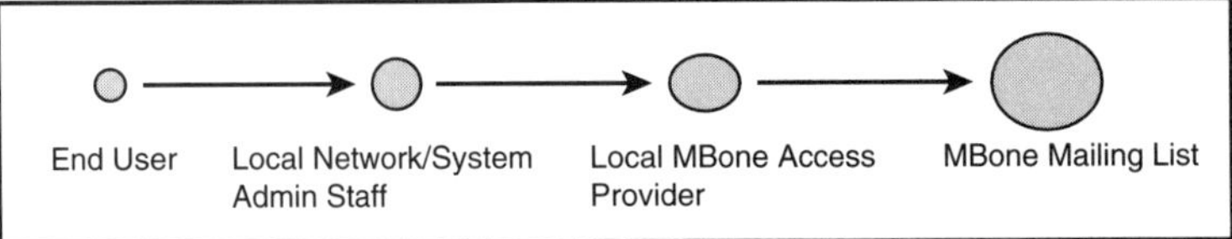

Table 5.2

MBone Service Providers

NSP	MBone Service Provider	Contact Person
ANSnet/AOL	ANS	Bob Enger, +1 703 758 7722, +1 202 215 2222, enger@reston.ans.net
ANSnet/AOL	ARPA (via ANS)	Brian Miller, +1 703/812-4723, mbone@copernicus.hpc.org
ANSnet/AOL	PREPnet	Jon Boone, +1 412 268-7874, boone@prep.net
MCInet	BARRNet	+1 415 934-2655 , noc@barrnet.net
MCInet	CAnet	CAnet Operations: +1 416 978 3328, noc@canet.ca CAnet Eng: canet-eng@canet.ca, Eric Carroll, eric@canet.ca.
MCInet	CICnet	Kraig Owen, +1 313 998-6520, mbone@cic.net
MCInet	JvNCnet	+1 609 897 7300, neng@jvnc.net, multicast@jvnc.net
MCInet	MichNet	Larry Blunk, +1 313 763 6056 , ljb@merit.edu, mbone@merit.edu
MCInet	MIDnet	Steve Schallehn, +1 800 937 6431, mbone@mid.net
MCInet	MRNet	Dave Bergum, +1 612 342 2895, bergum@mr.net
MCInet	NC-REN	Tim Seaver, +1 919 248 1973, mbone@ncren.net

NSP	MBone Service Provider	Contact Person
MCInet	NEARnet	NEARnet urgent/operations, +1 617 873 8730, nearnet-ops@nic.near.net
		NEARnet L. Sean Kennedy, +1 617 873 8730, nearnet-eng@nic.near.net NEARnet: Henry Clark, +1 617 873 4622, henryc@bbnplanet.com
MCInet	PREPnet	Jon Boone, +1 412 268 7874, boone@prep.net
MCInet	Sesquinet	Stan Barber, + 1 713 285 5415, mbone@sesqui.net
		Cathy Foulston, +1 713 285 5233, mbone@sesqui.net
MCInet	SURAnet	Erik Sherk, +1 301 982 3214, multicast@sura.net
		Walter Leskuski, +1 301 982 3214, multicast@sura.net
Sprintlink	Sprintlink/ICM	SprintLink/ICM Information/Problems: insc@sprint.net +1 800 669 8303, +1 703 689 6393
		SprintLink/ICM Engineering: engineer@sprint.net, mbone@sprint.net
		SprintLink/ICM Engineering: Sean Doran, +1 703 709 8743
Sprintlink	MIDnet	Steve Schallehn, +1 800 937 6431, mbone@mid.net
Sprintlink	MSC	Mike Spengler, +1 612 337 3557, mks@msc.edu, mbone@msc.net
Sprintlink	OARnet	Henry Clark, +1 614 728 8100, henryc@oar.net, oarnet-mbone@oar.net
		John Wieronski, +1 614 728 8100, ronski@oar.net, oarnet-mbone@oar.net

continues

Table 5.2, Continued

MBone Service Providers

NSP	MBone Service Provider	Contact Person
Sprintlink	WESTnet	Chris Garner, +1 303 492 3873, mbone@westnet.net, cgarner@westnet.net
Federal Networks	ESnet	ESnet Information: routing@es.net ESnet Problems: trouble@es.net
	NCInet	NCInet Ron Broersma, +1 619 553 2294, ron@nosc.mil
	NSI	Dan Evans, +1 415 604 0045, mbone-nsi@nsipo.nasa.gov
Independent Service Providers	Alternet	+1 703 204 8020, mbone-request@uunet.uu.net +1 703 204 8020, noc@uunet.uu.net
ISP	CERFnet	Pushpendra Mohta, +1 619 455 3900, mbone@cerf.net
ISP	Netcom	+1 408 551 2160, mbone@netcom.com
ISP	PSI	Mark Fedor, +1 703 904 4100, fedor@nisc.psi.net

An updated list of such MBone service providers is maintained by Matt Mathis, and is available at the following:

`http://www.psc.edu/~mathis/contacts.html`

A separate list of MBone service providers in Europe is available at:

`ftp://ftp.nic.surfnet.nl/surfnet/net-management/mbone/eucontacts.txt`

or

`http://www.cs.ucl.ac.uk/mice/`

For Japan, the MBone service contacts are as follows:

Tokuda & Murai Laboratory, Keio University, Japan
Hiroyuki Kusumoto
+81-466-49-1090
kusumoto@wide.ad.jp

Nippon Telephone and Telegraph (NTT):
Hitoaki Sakamoto
hitoaki@mahler.ntt.jp

If you cannot find names or contacts for MBone service providers from the preceding information, then you can seek help via the appropriate MBone mailing list.

Popular MBone Events

The MBone has been used since its early days for multicasting live shows, such as the Geek of the Week interviews, NASA space shuttle launches, and Internetworking workshops, seminars, and conferences. So far, many of these events have catered to the tastes of a small elite engineering community. Lately, however, the nature of events on the MBone have been varied, including professional and amateur music concerts, movies, and even Singapore's National Day parade—all live. The author himself has been contacted several times by various organizations to help them multicast classic Hollywood movies and produce commercials of certain products for MBone viewers. Almost all of these events today use the MBone tools described in Chapter 4, "MBone Multimedia Applications."

The live multicast of such events requires viewers and users to follow the rules associated with bandwidth use, as well as event specific etiquette, including the following:

- What not to do during the multicast
- How to access the multicast live media on your desktop
- Whether or not viewers are allowed to interrupt the event (for example, to ask questions)
- Where to get more detailed information about the event and its organizers

Event organizers use electronic means such as e-mail and Web-based communication to keep viewers and listeners informed about schedules and rules of etiquette to follow during the event multicast.

In this section, you will examine several events that took place over the MBone in the last few years. Hopefully, this will give you an idea of the potential uses of the MBone.

The Rolling Stones Concert

The Rolling Stones multicast 25 minutes of their Dallas Cotton Bowl concert live over the global MBone on November 18th, 1994, as a promotion for their television pay-per-view offer to North America on November 25th, 1994. It was organized as a brief event so as not to occupy the MBone bandwidth for a long time. The event raised many eyebrows because it was perceived by MBone users as crass commercialism of the Net. The organizers, on the other hand, did not seem to suggest otherwise.

In any case, the MBone multicast began on Friday, November 18th, at 10:00 p.m. EST. Not everything went well, however. Just before the Stones concert started, an unannounced renegade band called Severe Tire Damage (STD) started warming up using the same MBone channel. They started their warm-up set at 9:30 EST, just before the do-or-die live video feed came via satellite from the Cotton Bowl.

This event showed both the power and dangers of two-way loosely controlled interactivity of the MBone and the tools. But overall, it brought huge audience to the live MBone show all around the world. It also generated a lot of press and publicity for the MBone, Stones, and STD in the popular media.

More information on this event is available via the Web site:

```
http://www.stones.com/
```

The Severe Tire Damage (STD) Concerts

Severe Tire Damage claims to have been around since 1989, playing gigs at parties, clubs, and in the streets of Palo Alto, California. The band plays a variety of popular music, primarily rock and roll tunes—overall, they are a fun amateur music band. The author himself has seen STD perform online via the MBone, and says that they seem to know how to rock. The band plays mainly covers, but claims to have written and played over a dozen original songs. Their main claim to fame so far has been when they virtually opened the Stones concert with their own tunes on the same MBone channel. They have also been covered in the press—in local newspapers and public television.

The band plays regularly on the MBone every Wednesday at 9:00 p.m. PST, and the audio and video traffic goes all around the world (TTL 127). The band has regular listeners in

Japan and Finland. The band members develop and make use of very creative pieces of technology to allow viewers and listeners to control the camera and voice mixer remotely via the Web using Mosaic.

The core group consists of four members, as follows:

- Russ Haines—guitar and vocals
- Mark Manasse—bass and vocals
- Steven Rubin—vocals
- Mark Weiser—drums

Mark Weiser also happens to be the guiding light behind the ubiquitous computing world. His day job includes working as the Director of the Computer Science Lab at the famous Xerox PARC, in Palo Alto, California. More information on the band and their schedules is available at the following:

```
http://www.ubiq.com/std/band.html
```

World Radio Network

Internet Multicasting Service (IMS), a Washington D.C.-based non-profit organization, has been serving up audio via the Internet continuously since the first Geek of the Week program went online on March 30, 1993. Their programs deal with a diverse range of subjects including technology and society, arts and enjoyment, and public affairs.

IMS provides regular live multicasting feeds, including the U.S. Congress when in session. It also multicasts the *World Radio Network* (WRN) newsfeed—the new prestige radio service from Europe. WRN radio news is multicast live on the MBone 24 hours a day, all year long, using VAT and SD tools (see fig. 5.3). WRN has a round-the-clock schedule of top-quality news and varied programming from the leading public radio services of over 20 countries, including Austria, Australia, Belgium, Britain, Canada, Finland, France, Germany, Ireland, Israel, Korea (South), The Netherlands, Poland, Russia, Sweden, Switzerland, United Nations, Vatican, and South Africa. In addition, Radio Japan will soon be joining these radio services.

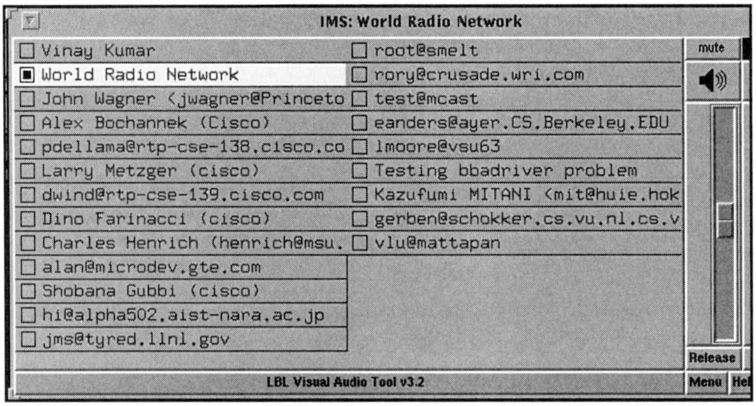

Figure 5.3

The WRN channel, accessed via the VAT tool.

Currently the WRN multicast audio feed is limited in access to continental United States only, for reasons of limited cross-continental Internet link bandwidth. For information, contact the following:

World Radio Network
Wyvil Court, 10 Wyvil Road
Vauxhall, London
SW8 2TG, England
Voice: 011 44 171 896 9000
Voice: 202 414 3185 (Local access number for North America)
E-mail: `online@wrn.org`
URL: `http://town.hall.org/Archives/radio/Mirrors/WRN/welcome.html`

NASA Shuttle Launches

The *National Aeronautics and Space Administration* (NASA) organizes space shuttle launches into space on a regular basis. These magnificent sights are made available live via real-time audio and video feeds by NASA to thousands of MBone viewers worldwide. MBone users use SD, VAT, and NV tools to log into such multicasts as they happen on a regular basis.

At the time of this writing, NASA was preparing for the 11-day STS-69 space mission and making arrangements for a live audio and video feed for MBone viewers. A detailed summary of NASA's mission objectives can be found via the Web site at:

`http://www.ksc.nasa.gov/shuttle/missions/missions.html`

Internet IETF Meetings

The MBone grew out of a small testbed that was created over DARTNet in 1992 to conduct IETF meetings using the mini IP multicast backbone and voice conferencing tools such as VAT. Thus, the IETF meetings seem to arouse emotional and historical feelings from most Internet engineers on the MBone. Almost all IETF meetings since March 1992 have been multicast live over the MBone. These meetings are physically conducted in different cities in different countries every quarter. Each meeting lasts for several days, more than eight hours a day, and almost all of the entire workshops are multicast live. The IETF workshop organizers typically use Sun and SGI workstations, along with MBone tools such as VAT, NV, WB, and SD. Each site is connected locally to an MBone service provider via a T-1 (1.54 Mbps) link.

Often, participants who cannot make it to the meetings tend to participate remotely from their offices and homes. Most people who cannot afford to leave their offices all the time find this really convenient by tuning in and out of these meetings from office desktop computers. More information on IETF activities and upcoming IETF meetings is available via the following:

```
http://www.ietf.reston.va.us/
```

MBone-Related Research Projects

There are several networking and multimedia projects that are on trial worldwide. Most of these projects are focused on upgrading the communication infrastructure to support bandwidth-intensive and time-critical data. Collaborative and social computing, medical imaging, weather data analysis and access, and groupware are some of the application areas for these projects. The following section examines a few projects that the author thinks most readers should be aware of in terms of their impact on the global Internet and, eventually, the MBone.

Global SchoolHouse Project—United States

The Global Schoolhouse Project was funded in part by the National Science Foundation and supported by many local and national businesses. The project aimed at connecting schools and students nationally and internationally using the Internet, and modeling classroom applications of Internet tools and resources.

Collaborative research was conducted between the schools, and students were found to interact via a variety of Internet tools, including live video conferences using Macintosh and Windows PCs (80386/80486-based). The live video conferencing between schools was conducted over the Internet using the popular CU-SeeMe software. Voice conferencing was done using either the traditional telephone circuits, or via the Internet using the Maven or the audio capabilities in the CU-SeeMe software. Last year, the Global Schoolhouse Project included schools from California, Illinois, Iowa, Missouri, Nebraska, New York, North Carolina, Tennessee, Utah, Vermont, and Virginia. Global Schoolhouse affiliate schools (schools that have adopted the Global Schoolhouse model) include schools in Washington and Australia. The Global Schoolhouse Project officially ended on December 29, 1994.

For further information, contact the following:

Yvonne Andres
Global SchoolNet Foundation
7040 Avenida Encinas 104-281
Carlsbad, CA 92009
Voice: (619) 439-0914 or (619) 757-6061
Fax: (619) 931-5934
E-mail: `andresyv@cerf.net`
URL: `http://k12.cnidr.org/gsh/gshwelcome.html`

The MICE Project—Europe

In 1992, a one-year project called The Piloting of Multimedia Integrated Services for European Researchers (MICE) [5] [6] came into being. This ESPRIT project completed Phase I in early 1994, but work is continuing within the initial collaborating group. Altogether, the project ran from December 1992 to September 1995. The consortium, with University College London (UCL) as the coordinating partner, consists of the following:

- Belgium—Free University of Brussels (ULB)
- France—INRIA Sophia Antipolis
- Germany—GMD Darmstadt
- RU.S. Stuttgart Norway University of Oslo (UiO)
- Norway—University of Oslo (UiO)
- Norwegian Telecom Research (NTR)
- Sweden KTH

- Swedish Institute of Computer Science (SICS)
- United Kingdom—University College London (UCL)

The goal of the MICE project was to pilot Internetworking between European researchers, and also to connect them to sites in the U.S., using existing network facilities. MICE piloted and supported a suite of tools that ran on modern Unix workstations. This suite allowed multimedia conferencing (audio, video, and shared workspace) between conference rooms and workstation-based facilities, hardware and software codecs, packet-switched networks, and ISDN, using both IP unicast (point-to-point) and IP multicast (multi-point) technology.

During the trial phase in 1993, Internetworking between the MICE partners and sites in the U.S., was demonstrated successfully in public events at several conferences, such as the IETF meetings, and the INET/JENC conference in Prague in 1994.

In October 1993, the MICE project started the MICE International Seminar Series on Multimedia, Communications and Networks, Distributed Systems and CSCW, with UCL and SICS as the principal transmitting sites, along with GMD (Germany), INRIA (France), and LBL (U.S.). These meetings and seminars were conducted using the MBone tools detailed in Chapter 4.

The MICE partners are working to improve the existing software tools for audio, video, and shared workspace to allow better use of both workstations and conference rooms. Current investigations are focused on the following issues:

- Internetworking with multimedia servers
- Security
- Traffic monitoring, modeling, and management
- Moving to high-speed networks

For further information, contact:

Professor Peter Kirstein
Department of Computer Science
University College London
London WC1E 6BT
Voice: +44 171 380 7212 Fax: +44 171 387 1397
E-mail: `p.kirstein@cs.ucl.ac.uk`
E-mail: `mice-nsc@cs.ucl.ac.uk`
URL: `http://www.cs.ucl.ac.uk/misc/`

NERO Project—United States

Network for Education and Research in Oregon (NERO) is a project of the *Oregon Joint Graduate Schools of Engineering* (OJGSE). Participants include the Oregon Center for Advanced Technology Education, Oregon Graduate Institute, Oregon Health Sciences University, Oregon State University, Portland State University, and the University of Oregon. Funding is provided by NASA research grant, OJGSE, and industry partnerships.

The main purpose of NERO is to facilitate collaborative research and teaching among the engineering and computer science faculty of the member institutions and with their counterparts at industrial sites, especially in high technology, software, and computers. Ancillary goals include outreach to K–12 educational institutions, small businesses, and communities.

The vision for the NERO project is high-speed, high-bandwidth data connections (including digital video and audio) within and between the OJGSE sites (Oregon State University, Oregon Graduate Institute, Portland State University, University of Oregon, the Biological Information Center at Oregon Health Science University, and the Oregon Center for Advanced Technology), with similar links to high-technology industrial partners. When additional capacity is added and where appropriate, outreach to small business and the community college educational system is also included.

The NERO network presently connects Portland, Beaverton, Corvallis, and Eugene, Oregon, with a wide-area *Asynchronous Transfer Mode* (ATM) network. Plans are underway in connecting NERO to the Internet at high speed (45 Mbps) and possibly to other ATM networks, such as BAGNet, at OC3 (155 Mbps). NERO is using Cisco Systems routers to connect legacy LANs into the U.S. WEST or GTE public service ATM switches, which provide the wide-area connectivity. For local ATM transport at each campus, ATM switches are being deployed to support 155 Mbps network capacity to the computer desktop.

NERO is using Sun SPARCstations for ATM testing, network management, and multimedia MBone applications, and to create a shared computing environment. NERO also developed a custom version of the MBone videoconferencing software NV (or NetVideo) to run on ATM networks. The software is called nvATM and is available for free from NERO's anonymous FTP site.

For further information, contact:

Tad Reynales or Janaka Jaywardena
Voice: +1 503 737 5235
Fax: +1 503 737 3462
E-mail: `info@nero.net`
URL: `http://www.nero.net/`

PEARnet–Japan

Pacific East Asia Research Network (PEARnet) is an effort by the Japanese telephone company *Nippon Telephone and Telegraph* (NTT) to create a high-speed Internetwork between Musashino, Japan, and Palo Alto, California. Currently, the PEARnet network is supported via a 23B+D ISDN line and one T1 leased line with combined bandwidth of up to 3 Mbps. This network is intended to be a cross-continental backbone infrastructure and provider of value-added rich services to users in Japan, Asia, and the United States. PEARnet runs the IP protocol suite and several MBone services. The PEARnet configuration is shown in figure 5.4.

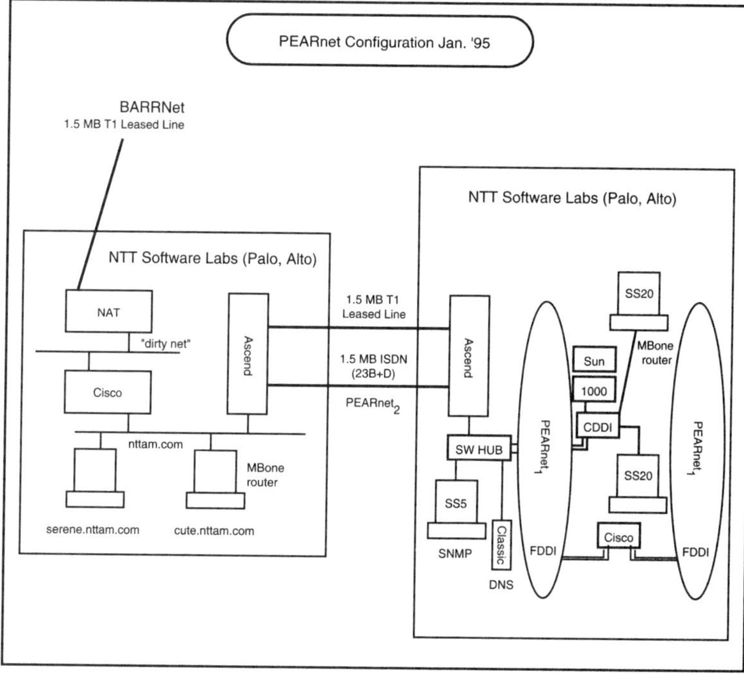

Figure 5.4

The PEARnet current configuration.

The PEARnet effort is subdivided into several smaller subprojects, such as EColabor, COGENT, Japan Window, and City Source. Teams of engineers collaborate in real-time using audio, video, shared screens, and documents using the PEARnet MBone. One of the goals of this project is to evaluate the usability and benefits of such wide-area, high-speed networking to support collaborative interactions. The focus of this is on the technical aspects, such as network delays and bandwidth-on-demand via ISDN; the social aspects, such as language differences and styles of interactions; and intangibles, such as the sense of community provided by tele-presence issues being researched.

For further information, contact:

Jeffrey D. Smith
Nippon Telephone & Telegraph
Software Labs.
250 Cambridge Avenue, Suite 201
Palo Alto, CA 94021
E-mail: sumisu@nttlabs.com
URL: http://www.ntt.jp/

Tenet and Sequoia 2000 Network–United States

The Sequoia 2000 network employs the Tenet protocol suite at each of its hosts and routers, making it one of the first wide-area packet-switched networks to provide end-to-end per-connection performance guarantees.

The Tenet communication protocol suite supports guaranteed performance communication in an Internet environment. It differs from the current IP suite, however, in that it is based on a connection-oriented, reservation-based scheme. The Tenet suite claims to protect the real-time connections even under heterogeneous heavy load. The Tenet suite coexists with current TCP/IP—it adds two extra networking stacks, called *Real-Time Internet Protocol* (RTIP) and *Real-Time Channel Admin Protocol* (RCAP), to facilitate real-time behavior.

The Sequoia 2000 network connects researchers in several sites within California. The topology of this network is shown in figure 5.5.

Sequoia researchers are investigating methods for providing both real-time as well as best-effort media services on this network. Real-time services are required by media types, such as audio and video, whereas best-effort scheme fits traditional data types, such as text and graphics. Today, the Sequoia network is being used to query and access remote satellite weather data, live audio and video conferences, and so forth. Some of the MBone tools, such as VAT and VIC, have been customized to run over the Sequoia network as well. This project is being done by students and faculty members at the University of California, Berkeley, and the *International Computer Science Institute* (ICSI), Berkeley. More details on this project are available in [2] (see bibliography).

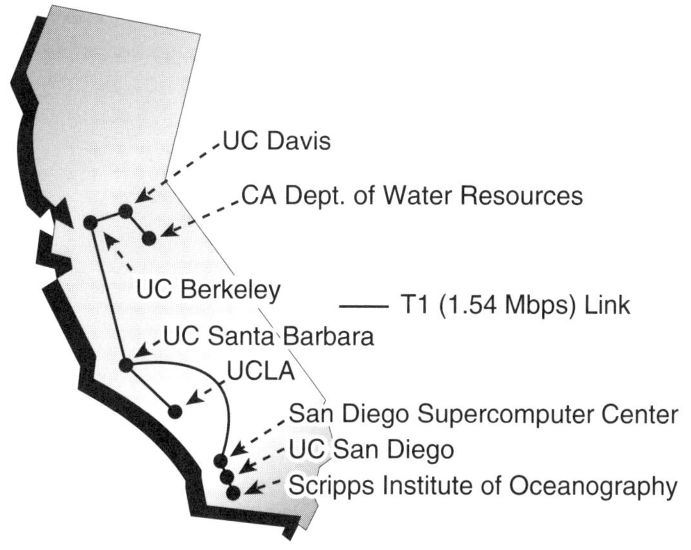

Figure 5.5

The Sequoia 2000 network.

For further information, contact:

Professor Domenico Ferrari
Tenet Project
Dept. of Computer Science
University of California at Berkeley
E-mail: `www@tenet.berkeley.edu`
URL: `http://tenet.berkeley.edu/`
URL: `http://www.sdsc.edu/0/Parts_Collabs/S2K/s2k_home.html`

JANET/SuperJANET–England

JANET/SuperJANET is the national academic community network in the United Kingdom. It is based on fiber-optic lines currently supplied by British Telecom. Fourteen sites are connected with PDH, running at 140 Mbps and multiplexed into four 34 Mbps tributaries. During late 1995 and early 1996, these lines will be replaced by 155 Mbps SDH lines. The pilot projects include a national full-screen full-motion video service using hardware codecs and 2 Mbps PVCs, development of an IP over ATM service, and ATM experiments. In addition to the ATM services, approximately 60 additional sites are connected by SMDS, with connectivity speeds reaching up to 10 Mbps.

Applications come from many disciplines and include distance learning, interactive browsing of datasets, and control of supercomputer simulations. The video pilot is used for multisite video conferencing to support national meetings and the teaching of medicine and surgery. MBone applications, such as workstation-based video conferencing and shared whiteboards, are in use at many sites.

For further information, please contact:

United Kingdom Education and Research Networking Association (UKERNA)
The Atlas Centre
Chilton, Didcot, Oxfordshire
OX11 0QS
Voice: +44 1235 822212
Fax : +44 1235 822399
E-mail: JANET-Liaison-Desk@UKERNA.AC.UK
URL: http://www.ja.net/

BAGNet

The *Bay Area Gigabit network* (BAGNet) is a high-speed Internetwork connecting several sites in California. Fourteen organizations in the San Francisco Bay Area are working with the Pacific Bell Broadband Strategy and Product Development Group to develop and deploy a large-scale ATM wide-area network. PacBell has granted the funding for this project for two years under the CALREN (CALifornia Research and Educational Network) grant. This network investigates the computer multimedia network infrastructure needed to support a diverse set of distributed applications, such as multimedia teleseminars, weather imaging, and virtual reality in such an environment.

The BAGNet community has agreed that BAGNet will use IP as the common network layer; it appears to participating hosts as a single IP subnet. Showcase applications such as teleseminars will use IP and IP multicast/MBone. The MBone-based seminars are regular features that use real-time multiple audio, video, and shared document streams for sharing and interacting remotely. The MBone traffic generated out of BAGNet is limited in scope within the BAGNet zone so as not to cause any permanent congestion at certain nodes or routers in the rest of the Internet. MBone traffic uses the DVMRP scheme for IP multicast packet routing.

Initially the network connections are via *Synchronous Optical NETwork* (SONET) OC-3 (155 Mbps) links [4]. Some of the participants anticipate upgrading to OC-12 (622 Mbps) as soon as possible, in order to support scientific applications requiring higher bandwidth.

For more information, contact the following:

Bill Johnston, wejohnston@lbl.gov
Lawrence Berkeley National Laboratory, Berkeley, CA

Marjory Johnson, mjj@riacs.edu
RIACS/NASA Ames Research Center, Mountain View, CA

Dan Swinehart, swinehart.parc@xerox.com
Xerox Palo Alto Research Center, Palo Alto, CA

Conferences, Journals, and Magazines

As of the time of this writing, there aren't any specific trade magazines, journals, or conferences dedicated entirely to the topic of MBone. In this section, however, the author has made an attempt to pick out a few of these that are close to presenting issues relating to the MBone technology, tools, and their use. Currently, the best bet is probably this book, all the online information that is available on the Net, and Internet RFCs and Internet drafts, although the last category may be hard to read and understand. Here is a brief collection of what helped the author the most during the course of writing this book.

Conferences and Workshops

The following is a list of conferences and workshops that are organized almost each year and cover technologies relating to topics such as multimedia, real-time networking, and internetworking. Most of these conferences are advertised in advance in most Internet and multimedia-related journals and magazines:

1. ACM Multimedia Conference
2. The Interop Conference
3. SPIE Multimedia Computing and Networking Conference
4. SIGGRAPH Conference
5. IEEE International Conference on Multimedia Computing and Systems
6. ACM SIGCOMM Conference
7. IEEE INFOCOM conference
8. IEEE Workshop on Enabling Technologies: Infrastructure for Collaborative Enterprises

Journals

The names of the journals mentioned here are quite technical in nature. These journals deal with internal specifications and state of the art research in the field of multimedia, Internet, and telecommunication technologies. Subscription to these journals may require you to become member of the affiliate organizations such as ACM, IEEE, and so forth:

1. Communications of the ACM, A monthly publication of the Association for Computing Machinery. For information:

   Voice: +1 212 869 7440
   URL: `http://www.acm.org/catalog/journals/10109300.html`

2. Multimedia Systems, ACM Press and Springer-Verlag. For information:

   Voice: +1 800 342 6626 or +1 212 626 0500
   URL: `http://www.acm.org/catalog/journals/11809300.html`

3. Proceedings of International ACM Multimedia Conference, ACM Press. For information:

   URL: `http://www.acm.org/catalog/proceedings/mm.html`

4. IEEE (Institute of Electrical and Electronics Engineers) Computer Magazine, a monthly publication for IEEE Computer Society members, Computer Society Press. For information:

   Voice: +1 800 CS BOOKS
   URL: `http://info.computer.org/pubs/computer/computer.htm`

5. IEEE Multimedia Magazine, Computer Society Press. For information:

   Voice: +1 800 CS BOOKS
   URL: `http://info.computer.org/pubs/multimed/multimed.htm`

Trade Magazines

These trade magazines are mainly focused on commercial activities that are going on around the world in the field of information technology—specifically the Internet, TCP/IP, multimedia, and networking-related product companies. Subscriptions to most of these magazines are free:

1. *InfoWorld Magazine*. For information:

   Voice: +1 800 227 8365, +1 415 572 7341
   URL: `http://www.infoworld.com/`

2. *LAN TIMES Magazine*. For information:

   Voice: +1 415 513 6800,
   E-mail: `susan_briedenbach@wcmh.com`

3. *Interactive Week Magazine*, Ziff Davis Publishing. For information:

   URL: `http://www.interactive-week.com/`

4. *Communications Week Magazine*

5. *Videomaker Magazine*, for audio/video equipment enthusiasts. For information:

   Voice: +1 619 745 2809
   URL: `http://www.videomaker.com/`

6. *Interactive Age Magazine*, a CMP publication. For information:

   Voice: +1 516 562 7383,
   URL: `http://techweb.cmp.com/ia/`

7. *Computer Video Magazine*, JRS Publishing. For information:

   Voice: +1 703 998 7600.

8. *MicroPublishing News*, Micro Publishing Press. For information:

   Voice: +1 310 371 5787,
   E-mail: `mpn@designlink.com`

9. *PC Magazine*, Ziff Davis Publishing. For information:

   Voice: +1 212-503-5100
   URL: `http://www.zdnet.com/~pcmag/`

10. *PC Week*, Ziff Davis Publishing. For information:

    URL: `http://www.zdnet.com/~pcweek/`

Chapter Summary

In this chapter, you have examined how best to utilize the MBone, where to look for the right kind of information relating to the MBone, and then how to use that information. As is quite clear, there isn't a real one-stop shop for MBone software, information, and services outside of this book. By the time this book is released, however, this current state most likely will have changed for the better.

chapter 6

System Administrator's Guide to the MBone

Now that you know enough about the underlying MBone technology and various applications and their use, it is time for you to take a look at what it takes for an organization to install such technology for corporate use. Most organizations today have a variety of computers that they use. In most cases, it is not one kind of computer or operating system that is being used; the corporate computing environment might consist of one or more of the following brands of computers and operating systems:

- PCs running DOS, DOS and Windows 3.1+, Windows NT, and Windows 95
- PCs running SolarisX86, Linux, and FreeBSD or BSDI Unix
- SUN workstations running SunOS 4.1.x and Solaris 2.x
- SGI workstations running IRIX5.2+
- DEC Alpha's running OSFV2.0+ and Windows NT
- IBM RS6000 running AIX3.2+
- HP workstations running HPUX and Windows NT

These are only some of the more popular platforms—there are others, of course. The same is true for the networking of computers. These computers could be interconnected on a LAN over Ethernet, FDDI, or CDDI running Novell NetWare, TCP/IP, or Novell IPX. With such a wide variety of choices and a heterogeneity in the office computing environment, how do you overlay an existing office computing infrastructure to support the MBone multimedia? Besides setting up, configuring, and debugging the MBone connection at your organization end, it is also important to see how to tie in security issues such as firewalls while accessing and providing rich multimedia content via the MBone. All such issues will be dealt with in this chapter.

The MBone Starter Kit

A few distinct issues need to be addressed before you install and use the MBone within your organization. These issues are as follows:

- Does each desktop in your organization support IP multicasting?
- Does your organization have a multicast router?
- Does each desktop user have access to the MBone applications for use?

The answers to such questions will be resolved in subsequent sections. The first issue deals with desktop users directly. It is the responsibility of the user or system administrator to see if an existing desktop supports IP multicasting (or IGMP) in the desktop operating system. If it does not, then the desktop needs to be configured appropriately for IP multicasting. There is no automatic way to find out if your operating system supports IP multicasting, however. Check the operating system manual to see if it supports IGMP or IP multicasting.

Configuring Desktop Computers for IP Multicasting

Getting each machine in your organization ready to send and/or receive multimedia data streams requires that the machine's operating system understands the class D addressed IP multicast packets. This will enable the machines to send and receive the MBone multimedia traffic. Besides sending and receiving the MBone data traffic from the network, support is also needed in rendering the multimedia traffic received to the user—for example, rendering video frames to the *Super Video Graphics Adaptor* (SVGA) display, to the television, or to the VCR. Such support requires the addition of proper multimedia hardware to your desktop workstation.

Therefore, for purposes of this chapter, you will learn to configure desktop machines for IP multicasting using the appropriate software first, followed by a discussion of the required hardware and multimedia support. These discussions will be broken down by computer operating systems.

IP Multicasting for Unix Computers

Most new Unix machines in the market come factory bundled with operating system support for IP multicasting or the IGMP inside the kernel. If you have an older machine, chances are that its operating system does not support IP multicast extensions. In that case, software for upgrading your Unix operating system kernel to support IP multicasting is available either from the workstation vendor or from one of the anonymous FTP sites that archives IP multicasting operating system kernel extensions.

Most computers that are connected to the MBone today have installed version 2.2 or higher of the multicast operating system kernel patches. Version 3.6 is the latest version that has been released at the time of writing this book.

If you have SUN workstations in your organization that are running the SunOS 4.1.x, you can get a copy of the IP multicast operating system kernel software extension version 3.5 for free via anonymous FTP using any FTP client on your desktop. The steps for downloading and unpacking the software for SunOS 4.1.x systems are described in Appendix A.

Only the system administrators and knowledgeable individuals should apply the kernel patches—the process of applying the patches assumes that you know how to configure and build a new operating system kernel. If you do not, then consult your system administrator to do this for you, or read the operating system's manual and documentation for your computer desktop.

The software distribution for IP multicast extensions from any of the FTP sites mentioned in Appendix A comes pre-bundled with a full set of instructions through a README-3.5 file on how to manually apply these version 3.5 patches to a standard SunOS 4.1.x kernel. A script called mcast_install also comes bundled with this distribution—it can automatically install these IP multicast patches for you. Instructions are also included on how to upgrade to version 3.5 of IP multicast kernel patches from previous versions—that is, version 3.3 and version 2.2. If you already have a machine with an older version of multicast operating system kernel, then you can upgrade easily as well.

Alternate FTP sites for version 3.5 of IP multicast kernel operating system patches are shown in table 6.1.

Table 6.1

FTP Sites for Version 3.5 of IP Multicast Extensions to SunOS 4.1.x

FTP Site	Directory	File Name
ftp.udel.edu	/pub/mbone/	ipmulti3.5-sunos41x.tar.Z
ftp.adelaide.edu.au	/pub/av/multicast/	ipmulti3.5-sunos41x.tar.Z
ftp.ucs.ed.ac.uk	/pub/video-conference/ipmulticast/	ipmulti3.5-sunos41x.tar.Z

If you have machines other than SunOS 4.1.x workstations, then you are out of luck as far as version 3.5 of the IP multicast kernel patches are concerned. Efforts are in progress, however, to make this version available for non-SunOS 4.1.x machines. By the time this book is published, one of the FTP sites listed in table 6.1 should have IP multicast kernel software for other Unix platforms as well.

IP Multicast Patches Version 3.3 to SunOS 4.1.x

The most widely used version for IP multicasting is version 3.3. It is fully compatible with the previous, as well as the new version 3.5. Most sites today use version 3.3 for their SunOS 4.1.x machines. This was the first version of IP multicast kernels that included a form of minimal *Resource Reservation Protocol* (RSVP) support. As a result, the multicast routers could now pre-allocate a certain amount of bandwidth for the MBone traffic. A list of FTP sites from which to access this version of IP multicast kernel patches is shown in table 6.2.

Table 6.2

FTP Sites for Version 3.3 of the IP Multicast Kernel Patches for the SunOS 4.1.x

FTP Site	Directory	File Name
ftp.adelaide.edu.au	/pub/av/multicast/	ipmulti3.3- sunos413x.tar.Z
ftp.ucs.ed.ac.uk	/pub/videoconference/ ipmulticast/	ipmulti3.3- sunos413x.tar.Z
parcftp.xerox.com	/pub/net-research/ ipmulti/historical	ipmulti3.3- sunos413x.tar.Z
ftp.uni-stuttgart.de	/pub/comm/multimedia/	ipmulti3.3- sunos413x.tar.Z

IP Multicast Patches: Version 3.3 to DEC-Ultrix

The version 3.3 kernel patches for the DEC-Ultrix 4.x operating system are available from the sites shown in table 6.3.

Table 6.3

FTP Sites for the DEC Ultrix IP Multicast Kernel Patches

FTP Site	Directory	File Name
ftp.adelaide.edu.au	/pub/av/multicast/	ipmulticast- ultrix4.1.patch.Z ipmulticast-ultrix4.2a-binary.tar.Z ipmulticast-ultrix4.2a.patch.Z
ftp.ucs.ed.ac.uk	/pub/video-conference/ ipmulticast/	ipmulti3.3-ultrix4.4-patch

Before you go on to explore various FTP sites for other Unix platforms, it is important to note that most new Unix workstations come with factory-built support for IP multicasting version 2.2 or higher in their operating system kernel. Therefore, you may not have to specifically configure your desktop machine for IP multicasting. Table 6.4 contains a listing of various versions of IP multicast kernel patches for different Unix operating systems.

Table 6.4

FTP Sites for IP Multicast Kernel Patches for Unix Systems

IP Multicast Version	Computing Platform	FTP Site	Directory	File Name
Version 2.2	HP-UX 9.01	ftp.ucs.ed.ac.uk	/pub/video-conference/ipmulticast/	hp-ipmulti.tar.Z
	SGI-IRIX 4.0x	ftp.ucs.ed.ac.	/pub/video-conference/ipmulticast/	ipmulti-sgi40x.tar.Z
	DEC-OSF1	ftp.ucs.ed ac.uk	/pub/video-conference/ipmulticast/	ipmulti-decosf1.tar.Z
	BSD 386	ftp.uni-stuttgart.de	/pub/comm/multimedia/1386/	bsd386-ipmcast.tar.Z
	SGI-IRIX 5.1+	fgi.sgi.com	/sgi/ipmcast/IRIX5/	irix5.3.tar.Z

IP Multicasting on Intel PCs Running Microsoft Windows/DOS

It is clear by now that IP multicast support is needed in the desktop operating system. In previous sections, such support in Unix environments was described. There is similar support available, however, for the popular MS Windows systems as well. In addition, Microsoft Corp. has announced support for IGMP into their Microsoft Windows NT and Windows 95 operating systems products. More information on Microsoft's support for IP multicasting in Windows NT and Windows 95 is available from Microsoft's anonymous FTP site, as follows:

```
%ftp ftp.microsoft.com
% Name: anonymous
% password: <login_name@org_name.com>
ftp>cd /bussys/WinSock/ms-ext/
ftp>bin
ftp>get MULTICAST.TXT
ftp>get winsock.h
ftp>get VXDTD1.DOC
```

```
ftp>get party.c
ftp>get party.exe
ftp>quit
```

The file winsock.h provides the multicast extensions for Win32. A sample multicast program in C with the names *party.c* and *party.exe* is also included in the distribution.

Another software company—FTP Software, Inc., an Internet company—has a TCP/IP stack product for MS Windows operating systems called PC/TCP® (3.0) and PC/TCP OnNet® (1.1), which supports IP multicast. Several developers have tested and used this product for building MBone software. More information on this product is available on the World Wide Web at the following URL:

```
http://www.ftp.com/mkt_info/advfeats.html
```

IP Multicasting for Macintosh Systems

Apple Computer, Inc. supports IP multicasting in its new MacOS-7.5.2. The new TCP/IP stack under the MacOS operating system is called Mac OpenTransport version 1.0b2, and follows the System V Unix-like network programming interface. The Mac OpenTransport replaces Apple's earlier MacTCP stack. Some documentation on IP multicasting support in the new MacOS 7.5.2, as well as their TCP/IP *Application Programming Interface* (API), is now available via anonymous FTP, as follows:

```
%ftp seeding.apple.com
% Name: anonymous
% password: <login_name@org_name.com>
ftp>cd /ess/public/opentransport/OT_Docs_textonly/
ftp>get OT_TCPIP
ftp>quit
```

Hardware Peripherals for the MBone Desktop

In order to be able to fully participate in the MBone multimedia sessions, desktop users need to be able to send and receive multimedia information. This includes voice, video, graphics, and text. Most desktop computers you buy in the market today have multimedia capabilities, but the older legacy models do not. Thus, in this section, you will find tips on adding such multimedia support to the user desktop.

RISC-Based Unix Workstations

Most Unix workstations come bundled with audio input and output hardware—therefore, there may not be a need to buy audio hardware. Most RISC-based Unix workstations support at least 8-bit, full-duplex operations. So what is a full-duplex operation?

As shown in figure 6.1, two main kinds of data flow schemes exist—the half-duplex and the full-duplex. In a half-duplex operation, data flows only in one direction at any given time between two or more endpoints, and each endpoint can either transmit or receive at any given time. In a full-duplex model, however, the communication endpoints can transmit and receive simultaneously—there is free flow of information in a bi-directional manner.

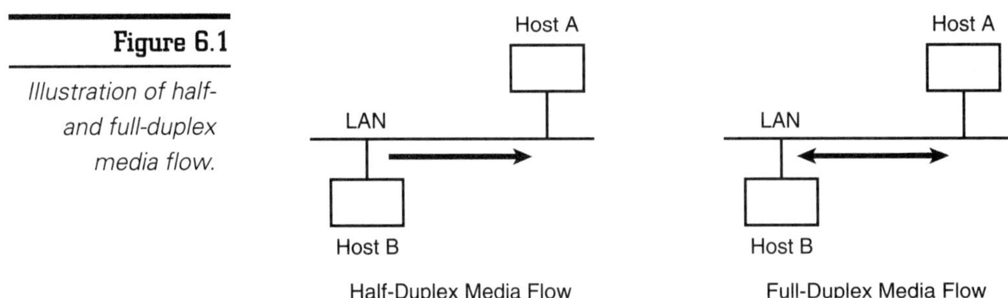

Figure 6.1

Illustration of half- and full-duplex media flow.

Full-duplex operation is very critical for doing two-way free-form voice conversations. Full-duplex operation allows input and output of voice data simultaneously. This is not essential, however, if your application demands only one-way operation (either input or output) at any given time. The next sections examine some of the live video grabber cards that are most commonly used on the MBone.

VigraPix Video Card

VigraPix Corp. makes a video digitizer board called the VigraPix card for the SUN workstations that plugs into the SBus of the workstation. It is a single-slot card designed to capture data from standard video sources. It includes one composite video and two S-video inputs; it is also capable of digitizing *National Television Standards Committee* (NTSC), *Phase Alternation Line* (PAL), and *Sequential Couleur A Memoire* (SECAM) signals to display still or live video on a standard SUN workstation. The VigraPix card also supports *NetVideo* (NV) video compression and decompression in hardware. As a result, it works very well with the NetVideo videoconferencing software by achieving higher quality video and faster frame rates (see Chapter 4, "MBone Multimedia Applications," for more information). This product supports libraries for SunOS 4.1.x and Solaris 2.x. More information on the product is available by contacting the following:

VigraPix Inc.
Division of VisiCom Laboratories
10052 Mesa Ridge Court
San Diego, CA 92121

World Wide Web: `http://www.vigra.com/`
Voice mail: +1-619-597-7080
Toll-free number: 1-800-66-VIGRA (1-800-668-4472)
E-mail: `sales@vigra.com`
Fax: +1-619-597-7094

PowerVideo and MultiVideo Cards

Parallax Graphics, Inc. makes a video grabber card called the PowerVideo card. It is an SBus card and supports real-time video capture, playback, and networking of high-quality digital video and still images, using hardware JPEG compression and decompression. This product also supports video output S-VHS to a VCR. For additional information on this product, contact the following:

Parallax Graphics, Inc.
2500 Condensa Street
Santa Clara, CA 95051
World Wide Web: `http://www.parallax.com/`
Phone: +1-408-727-2220
E-mail: `info@parallax.com`
Fax: +1-408-980-5139

DEC J300 Sound and Video Card for Alpha Workstations

The Digital Alpha workstations also support a lot of multimedia capabilities. The Alpha line of workstations from DEC come pre-bundled with the J300 sound and video digitizer board. The card supports full-motion video input in NTSC, PAL, and SECAM in both composite and S-video formats. Video can be captured and displayed on the workstation screen in 8-bit pseudo-color, 8-bit grayscale, or 24-bit true color formats.

The J300 video card can take the digital video stream on the computer workstation display and output it as NTSC or PAL video in S-video or composite formats to an analog videotape on a VCR. The card can also record such digital video data to writeable optical disc, or display on a TV monitor. JPEG video compression and decompression standard is supported in the J300 hardware itself. This helps MBone videoconferencing software such as NV or VIC to produce better performance in terms of quality of video reproduction and faster frame rates. The DEC J300 video card is priced at $2,795 (U.S.).

For a description of this software product, access the following FTP site on the Internet:

```
gatekeeper.dec.com under the directory /pub/DEC/Decinfo/SPD/
```

Information data sheets are available at the following FTP sites on the Internet:

`gatekeeper.dec.com under /pub/DEC/infosheets/sound-motion-j300.txt`

`gatekeeper.dec.com under /pub/DEC/infosheets/multimedia-services.txt`

SunVideo Frame Grabber Card

The SunVideo board is a SUN SBus card. Video connectors support two composite and one S-video input. The SunVideo card senses whether the source is NTSC or PAL and configures itself appropriately. A video RISC processor, the C-Cube CL4000, is used to perform compression in multiple standard formats: JPEG, MPEG-1, and Cell. Solaris version 2.3 or later release is supported. Contact your local SUN reseller for details, or get more information from the World Wide Web at the following:

`http://www.sun.com/smi/bang/SunVideo.html`

SUN VideoPix Card

The VideoPix Card from SUN is also an SBus card. It is the older generation card—slower, but cheaper than most current generation video digitizer boards that are out in the market. The VideoPix board does not support hardware-based video compression or decompression, but it performs fairly well with SunOS 4.1.x and the MBone video conferencing software such as NV and VIC. This product accepts NTSC, PAL, and S-video inputs. The Solaris 2.x version of the video libraries has also been ported, and it can be accessed via anonymous FTP from the following site:

`playground.sun.com under /pub/videopix/`

Silicon Graphics, Inc. also sells a video digitizer card called the Indigo Video Card. Similarly, Hewlett-Packard, Inc. sells the MediaMagic 700 video card on the market.

Intel Computers Running MS Windows

Although most of the traditional desktop PCs running MS Windows are multimedia PCs, the multimedia hardware in these PCs is designed to do only local multimedia and not networked multimedia. *Local multimedia* means playing and displaying multimedia files from the hard disk, the CD-ROM drive, and local direct input such as microphone or video camera. To play networked MBone multimedia, proper multimedia hardware is needed.

Voice digitizers should be full-duplexed if the desktop PC is to be used for MBone-based voice conferencing so that the boards can digitize voice from the microphone while playing back remote voice from the network such as the MBone. Generally, it might be difficult to get PC sound cards to do exactly 8 KHz, as these cards tend to support sampling frequencies that are 11.025 KHz, 22.1 KHz, and higher.

Gravis Ultrasound (GUS) Corp. sells various kinds of GUS sound digitizer boards. One of these is a higher-performance version called the UltraMax version 3.4, which records and plays back 16-bit voice up to 48 KHz with ADPCM, mu-law, and a-law voice compression. GUS voice cards cost about $200 (U.S.).

GUS FTP sites in North America are as follows:

```
archive.orst.edu under/pub/packages/gravis

wuarchive.wustl.edu under/systems/ibmpc/ultrasound
```

The ProAudio Spectrum voice digitizer card from Mediavision Corp. can be used for full-duplex audio. The card is full-duplex because it contains two sound boards in one—an 8-bit SoundBlaster, as well as the ProAudio Spectrum part. The Artisoft sound board also supports full-duplex voice and does mu-law voice encoding. Several other vendors sell sound boards as well—a few of them are listed in the following:

1. Adlib Multimedia, Inc.—sound hardware
   220 Grande Allee East, Suite 850
   Quebec, QC, Canada G1R 2J1
   Phone: 800-463-2686, +1-418-529-9676

2. Advanced Gravis Computer Technology Limited—sound hardware
   111-7400 MacPherson Ave.
   Burnaby, B.C., Canada V5J 5B6
   Main phone: 604-431-5020
   Support phone: 604-431-1807
   E-mail: `tech@gravis.com`
   Fax: 604-431-5155

3. Cardinal Technologies—sound hardware
   1827 Freedom Road
   Lancaster, PA 17601
   Phone: 717-293-3000

4. Covox, Inc.—sound hardware
   675 Conger Street
   Eugene, OR 97402
   Main: 503-342-1271
   BBS: 503-342-4135
   E-mail: `71333.167@CompuServe.com`
   Fax: 503-342-1283

5. Creative Labs/Brown Wagh (Soundblaster)—sound hardware
   2050 Duane Avenue
   Santa Clara, CA 95054
   Main: 408-428-6600
   Sales: 800-998-1000
   Support: 405-742-6622
   Fax: 405-742-6644 (742-6633?)

6. MediaVision, Inc. (ProAudio Spectrum)—sound hardware
   47221 Fremont Blvd
   Fremont, CA 94539
   Main: 800-348-7116 or 510-770-8600
   Sales: 800-845-5870
   Support: 800-638-2807 or 510-770-9905
   Fax: 510-770-8648 or 510-770-9592
   BBS: 510-770-0968 and 770-1661 (2400,8,N,1)
   510-770-0527 (9600,8,N,1)

7. Turtle Beach Systems—sound hardware
   Cyber Center, Unit 33, 1600 Pennsylvania Ave
   York, PA 17404
   Main: 717-843-6916
   E-mail: `75300.1374@CompuServe.com`
   (Turtle Beach*Roy Smith)
   Fax: 717-854-8319

The following section lists names and addresses of video card manufacturers and vendors. Before you go out and buy any video digitizer board on the market, ask at least the following questions about the board:

- Does the video card take NTSC Composite and S-video inputs? Is PAL video input support adequate?

- What pixel sizes are supported by the video card? Can the card support 512x512 video samples at 24-bits per pixel, as well as other sizes?

- Does the video card support hardware-based reduction of digitized video images to 8-bit color or grayscale modes?
- Does the card support hardware-based video compression and decompression algorithms such as H.261, JPEG, MPEG, NV, and so forth?
- Is there a video card-compatible software available that will enable you to display and save video images in color or grayscale—8-, 16-, or 24-bit color formats? What video and image formats are supported to save such files?

The video cards may support additional features as well, but the ones listed in the preceding are the key. Some video card manufacturers and vendors are as follows:

1. Digital Vision, Inc.(ComputerEyes/RT)—video hardware
   List price: $399.95 (U.S.)
   270 Bridge Street
   Dedham, MA 02026
   Voice: +1-617-329-5400
   E-mail: `digvis@tiac.net`
2. miro Computer Products, Inc. (miroVideo DC1 TV)—video hardware
   List price: $899 (U.S.)
3. Orchid Technology, Inc. (Orchid Vidiola Pro/D)—video hardware
   List price: $699 (U.S.)
4. Hauppauge Computer Works (Win/TV Cinema/TV-Celebrity/TV-HighQ)—video hardware
   List price: Cinema—$349, Celebrity—$449, HighQ—$499 (U.S.)
5. ATI Technologies Inc. (Video Basic, Video-It)—video hardware
   List price: $249, $499 (U.S.)

Macintosh Computers

The Macintosh computers have excellent multimedia support—almost all new Macs come factory built with all kinds of audio and video hardware and software. Unlike the Intel PC/Windows market, the Macintosh market is not as fragmented. As a result, users do not have to worry about buying and installing audio, video hardware, and driver software for the hardware, in addition to the application software itself. Most of the MacOS systems support full-duplex audio and video streams I/O. In case your Mac does not support the video digitizer card, the following lists a few you can buy on the market:

1. Video Spigot hardware
   List price: approximately $380

2. Digital Vision, Inc. (ComputerEyes/RT SCSI port digitizer)—video hardware
   List price: $599.99
   270 Bridge Street
   Dedham, MA 02026
   Voice: +1-617-329-5400
   E-mail: digvis@tiac.net

Video Cameras

In a multimedia MBone session involving real-time video, video cameras and VCRs act as the NTSC, PAL, and S-video video sources. These video sources feed input for the video digitizer boards that are connected to your desktop workstations. There are several analog video cameras that sell on the market, but some of them that have been tried in office desktop lighting conditions are mentioned here:

- Connectix, Inc. sells a popular $99 video camera for Macintosh computers called QuickCam. This portable camera works well as an NTSC video source for the Macintosh desktop.
- VideoLabs, Inc. sells FlexCam, a $600 CCD color video camera unit with a built-in flexible stand. This unit works fairly well for desktop conferencing.
- SonyTR-61 color palmcorder is a popular model.
- SGI Indy workstations come bundled with the IndyCam video cameras as well.

So far, you have learned about the desktop operating systems and their support for IP multicasting, and various multimedia hardware peripheral devices such as audio, video cards, and video cameras that are required to do multimedia interactions over the MBone. The next step is then to use the hardware and software mentioned in previous sections of this chapter to set up, configure, and debug an MBone connection at your local end.

Configure the Tunnel and the Mrouter

The first step toward setting up an MBone connection within your organization requires setting up an MBone tunnel at your end, followed by configuration of the multicast router so that the MBone multimedia packets can flow between your site and the rest of the MBone. As discussed in earlier chapters, the MBone information packets get routed between subnets over the MBone tunnels. The multicast router, also called the mrouter or mrouted (for multicast routing daemon), is responsible for forwarding such packets over the tunnels between different subnets.

The mrouted program is a software package that is available for free from the Internet FTP sites. These sites are usually the same ones as those used for IP multicast operating system kernel extension software. The mrouted program was designed and developed to run on any Internet server class Unix machines; plan to run the MBone router "mrouted" on an IP multicast-capable Unix machine on your local Net.

Before you run the mrouted program, the file /etc/mrouted.conf needs to be configured appropriately. The README file included in the software distribution that comprises the IP multicast operating system kernel patches describes how to configure the mrouted.conf file. A sample mrouted.conf file for IP multicast version 3.5 or greater looks like the following:

```
# name <boundname> <scoped-addr>/<mask-len>
# cache_lifetime 3600          # seconds
# pruning on
#
# phyint <local-addr> [disable] [metric <m>] [threshold <t>] [rate_limit <b>]
#                         [boundary (<boundname>¦<scoped-addr>/<mask-len>)]
#                         [altnet (<subnet>/<mask-len>¦<subnet>)]
# tunnel <local-addr> <remote-addr> [srcrt] [metric <m>]
#                                     [threshold <t>] [rate_limit <b>]
#                         [boundary (<boundname>¦<scoped-addr>/<mask-len>)]
#
#   NOTE: any phyint commands MU.S.T precede any tunnel commands
#   NOTE: the mask-len is the no. of leading 1's in the mask
#   NOTE: rate_limit is in kilobits, and defaults to 500 for tunnels
# Example of named boundary:
#name LOCAL 239.255.0.0/16
#name EE 239.254.0.0/16         # i.e. the EE dept wants local groups
#
# Example of use of named boundary
#phyint le1 boundary EE         # le1 is our interface to comp sci,
#                               # keep them away from our local groups
#
#
# Template tunnel
tunnel 128.4.0.77 128.4.0.8 metric 1 threshold 64 rate_limit 500  # <— REPLACE
#       boundary LOCAL
#
# You might want to specify a boundary on your tunnel to the outside world,
# as above.
```

Let's now describe all the commands that are listed in the preceding sample /etc/mrouted.conf file. The *Phyint* command precedes the tunnel command and is used to disable multicast routing on the specified network interface. The network interface may be described by the <local-addr>, or network interface type—that is, le0 (Lance Ethernet), ie0 (Intel Ethernet), and so forth. For multihomed hosts running as an mrouter, multicast routing could be disabled by specifying subnets via <altnet> keyword.

The *tunnel* command can be used to establish a tunnel link between local IP address <local-addr> of the mrouter and remote IP address <remote-addr> of the MBone service provider's mrouter.

The *rate_limit* option enables the network administrator to specify a certain bandwidth in Kilobits per second that would be allocated to multicast traffic. It defaults to 500 Kbps on tunnels, and 0 (unlimited) on physical interfaces.

The *boundary* option allows an interface to be configured as an administrative boundary for the specified scoped address. Packets belonging to this address will not be forwarded on a scoped interface. The boundary option accepts either a name or a boundary specification.

A sample /etc/mrouted.conf file may look like this:

```
#
# mrouted.conf example
#
# Name our boundaries to make it easier
name LOCAL 239.255.0.0/16
name MIS 239.254.0.0/16
#
# le1 is our gateway to HRD, don't forward our
#     local groups to them
phyint le1 boundary MIS
#
# le2 is our interface on the webgroup net, it has four
#     different length subnets on it.
# note that you can use either an ip address or an
# interface name
phyint 172.16.12.38 boundary MIS altnet 172.16.15.0/26
     altnet 172.16.15.128/26 altnet 172.16.48.0/24
#
```

```
# atm0 is our ATM interface, which doesn't properly
#      support multicasting.
phyint atm0 disable
#
# This is an internal tunnel to another MIS subnet
# Remove the default tunnel rate limit, since this
#   tunnel is over ethernets
tunnel 192.168.5.4 192.168.55.101 metric 1 threshold 1rate_limit 0
#
# This is our tunnel to the outside world. Be careful with those boundaries.
tunnel 192.168.5.4 10.11.12.13 metric 1 threshold 32
     boundary LOCAL boundary MIS
----------------------------------------------------------
```

After configuring the /etc/mrouted.conf file, now send a request to your local IP service provider for a tunnel. A sample e-mail request for establishing a tunnel between your organization and the global MBone may look like this:

To: mbone@isi.edu
From: <you>
Subject: Request for Tunnel
Cc: <your_local_mbone_service_provider>, <your_local_ip_service_provider>

I would like to add my site <mydomain.com> to the MBone via a tunnel. Here is how my tunnel endpoint configuration should look:

```
Mrouter machine configuration: SunSPARC10, SunOS        4.1.3_U1, sun4m
Multicast kernel patches applied: version 3.5
ftp://parcftp.xerox.com/pub/netresearch/ipmulti/ipmu    lti3.5-sunos41x.tar.Z
Mrouter machine (my tunnel endpoint) IP address:        192.100.x.x
```

The MBone administrator contact address is as follows:

Vinay Kumar
XYZ Inc.
5000 Page Mill Road
Redwood Park, CA 93333
Voice (daytime): +1-415-555-1212
E-mail: vinay@xyz.com

Any help in providing me with a tunnel will be greatly appreciated.

The contact points for all the MBone IP service providers worldwide are provided in Chapter 5, "MBone Resources."

After you receive a confirmation on your request from your MBone service provider, you may have to go back to the /etc/mrouted.conf file and edit it minimally to reflect the MBone provider's end of the tunnel. Once configured, you are now ready to start the mrouted daemon by typing the following command:

```
/etc/mrouted [-p] [-c config_file] [-d [debug_level]]
```

You do not have to run the mrouted if you do not want to route the IP multicast packets outside your local subnet. In addition, mrouted should not be run on the same machine that routes IP unicast packets—mrouted routes IP multicast packets only.

It is important to run the mrouted version 2.2 or higher. If you have not installed MBone yet, then you should install version 3.6 or higher—it is more efficient in terms of better bandwidth and network management, and also fixes problems from earlier versions.

If on using one of the MBone applications on a machine that has no multicast routes on it, then you may see the following error message:

```
IP_ADD_MEMBERSHIP: Can't assign requested address
```

This is fixed by doing one of the following. You need either a "default" route or a route to 224.0.0.0, which points to the network interface you want to use to send multicast packets. If your host only has one interface, run the following command as root:

```
route add 224.0.0.0 `your_local_hostname` 0
```

If you have more than one interface, replace the `hostname` with the host name or address for the interface you want to use.

If, on the other hand, you do not see any error messages on your screen, this means your MBone tunnel is almost up and running, and you may be connected to the MBone. How can you be sure that you are connected? You will find this out in the next section.

Testing Your MBone Connection

Once the tunnel can be configured at both ends—that is, your end, as well as your MBone service provider's end—it's time to do a few simple tests to see if you are connected to the MBone. There are two approaches to accomplish this. The simple approach is to run the MBone application software called the SD tool (see Chapter 4). Just type the following command on any IP multicast-enabled Unix machine connected to the same subnet as the mrouter:

```
sd &
```

You should see the SD window on your screen. Let the program run for a few minutes. If you see MBone session names such as "MBone Audio," "MBone Video," and "Radio Free Vat" begin to appear in the SD window, this means your MBone connection is up and running. The IP multicast packets, therefore, are flowing from the rest of the MBone to your subnet. This was the easy test. You can also test the MBone connection by running one of the MBone debugging tools explained later in the chapter. So, if you are up and running, you can feel free to use any of the MBone application software that is described in Chapter 4.

If you do not see anything in the SD window, however, then you know that there is a problem somewhere in the installation and configuration of the MBone tunnel, or in mrouted, either at your end or your MBone service provider's end. The best way to fix this is to use the MBone debugging tools to isolate the problem and read the manual (or help) pages that are included with the software that is being used. In addition, you can always consult the appropriate Internet mailing lists or product vendors for help.

Disabling the MBone Tunnel

If at any point in time your organization decides to disconnect from the MBone, then it is not a difficult process. The MBone architecture is very flexible in allowing such operations without affecting others on the MBone, except if you are an MBone service provider. As a result of tearing down your tunnel, the IP multicast traffic that flows over your MBone tunnel into and out of your subnet will be simply turned off. In order to do this, simply log in to the multicast routing machine on your subnet, find the process ID of the mrouted program, and kill the process. This can be done as follows on most Unix machines:

```
% ps -e ¦ grep mrouted
<This will output the process ID of the mrouted program>
% kill -9 <mrouted_process_id>
```

This will shut off the routing of IP multicast traffic to and from your subnet. Running the mrouted process again will re-establish the tunnel and the IP multicast traffic will start flowing smoothly again. It is thus easy to see that tearing down the tunnel and bringing it back up is not very difficult and can be done anytime. The MBone service providers should not do this, however, unless it is for very specific reasons. Tearing down a tunnel at the MBone service provider's end can easily affect other tunnels because one tunnel may feed IP multicast data streams into other tunnels or subnets.

Note that if your organization, your MBone service provider, and all the intervening IP routers use IP multicast routing-enabled hardware routers, such as Cisco System's Cisco-7000 router, then you do not need to follow the preceding instructions. Having native multicast routing in the hardware IP routers makes tunneling redundant—you therefore do not need MBone tunnels. The IP multicast packets get routed just like any other Internet packets because all the routers understand IP multicasting. You should consult the configuration manual provided by the router vendor to see how to configure such routers to connect to the MBone. In addition, consult with your MBone service provider to see what kind of router setup they have.

At this point, your organization is practically on the MBone. Before you begin using it, please carefully read the do's and don'ts that are described in detail in Chapter 4. Now that you and everyone else in your organization is ready to experience the MBone, let's take one hard look at some of the related issues, such as security and firewalls. As a result of hooking up your organization to the MBone, a special type of Internet traffic called IP multicast data now flows through your local subnet. To make sure that no rogue packets or hackers use this route to infiltrate your subnet, let us briefly describe the measures one can take to thwart such attempts. Of course, for detailed discussion on network security and Internet firewalls, you should read [1] and [2] (see bibliography).

Firewalls and Security on the MBone

Network security is an important issue in almost any kind of internetworking, be it e-mail, FTP, the Web, or the MBone. Malicious packets sent out by remote rogue applications or wily hackers can penetrate a completely open network and cause damage to your resources. The Internet routers are configured in a specific way to filter out unwanted and undesirable packet traffic. One such technique of configuring the routers to allow only harmless, useful traffic is called *router filtering*. These filters are often used to provide what is called a *firewall* between your local subnet (or domain) and the rest of the global Internet. Filters are generally intended to allow a select set of IP hosts and network applications to communicate across the domain boundary, providing the advantages of the Internet connectivity, while minimizing the exposure of internal resources. A simple configuration of a firewall-based network is shown in figure 6.2.

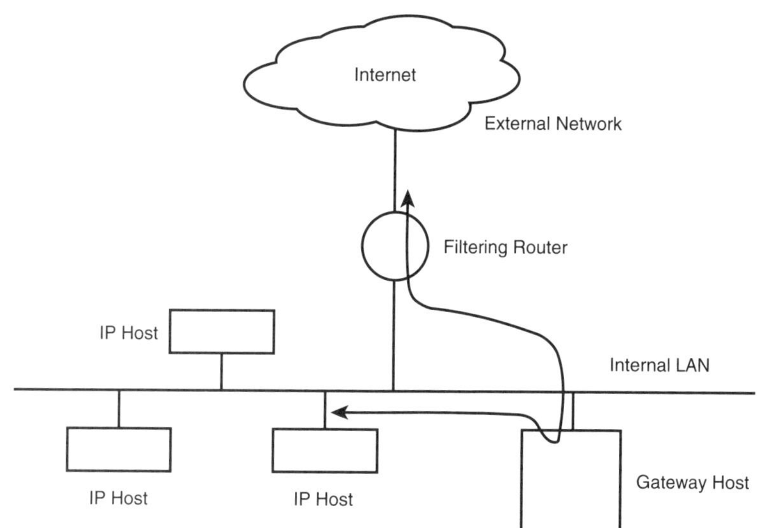

Figure 6.2

Securing an internal network via router filters and firewall gateways.

Previous work on defining gateway filters has concentrated on allowing communication between specific hosts or subnets (identified by IP source or destination addresses), providing access to specific source and destination addresses, and providing access to specific applications that are identified by IP protocol and port numbers. The following section looks at the router filter requirements for allowing IP multicast tunnels through a firewall gateway.

In Chapter 3, "A View Inside the MBone," you learned that there are two distinct types of IP packets associated with the MBone packet traffic:

- IGMP group membership and routing update packets
- IP multicast data packets

These types of packets are discussed in the following sections.

IGMP Packets

The IGMP membership query messages from the local mrouter, and the corresponding IGMP membership reports for active multicast groups from IP hosts on the subnet, are never propagated beyond the local subnet.

As shown in figure 6.3, the IGMP DVMRP routing update messages are exchanged between neighboring mrouters over an MBone tunnel, which presents two distinct cases. Messages exchanged between mrouters connected via a multicast-capable subnet are sent to the 224.0.0.4 multicast group, while neighbors connected via a tunnel unicast updates between tunnel endpoints. The multicast DVMRP updates are sent with a TTL of 1 and are not propagated beyond the local subnet. This leaves only the IGMP DVMRP tunnel-neighbor messages that cross the firewall boundary. These messages are identical for both "srcrt" and "encapsulated" tunnels (see Chapter 3 for definitions of srcrt and encapsulated tunnels). They can be easily identified by the IP source address and the IP destination address being the tunnel endpoints, and the IP protocol version number as 2—that is IGMP(2).

Figure 6.3

IGMP messages on the local subnet and over the MBone tunnel.

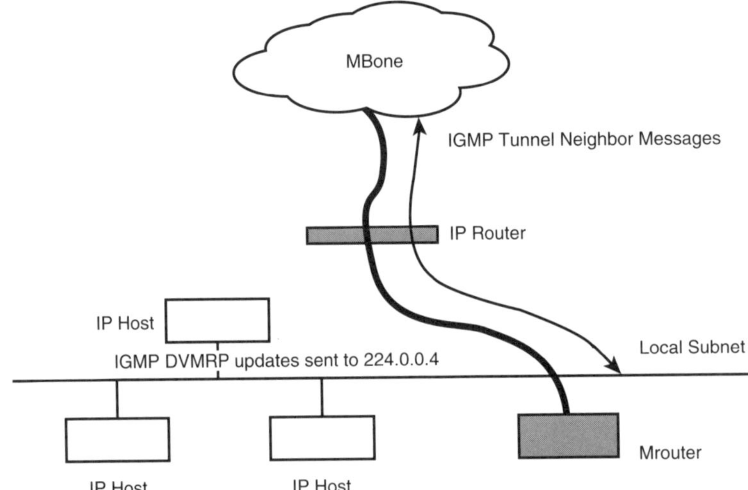

IP Multicast Data Packets

An IP multicast source on an IP host generates standard UDP/IP data packets, with the exception that the standard unicast IP destination address is replaced by a class D multicast address. These packets are then transmitted on a local multicast-capable subnet; it is the responsibility of the mrouters to forward these packets along the proper multicast distribution tree over the tunnel.

There are currently two forms of tunneling in use in the Internet today—those using an IP Loose *Source Route* option (srcrt), and those using IP-in-IP encapsulation (encapsulated). IP multicast packets traversing an encapsulated tunnel can be easily identified by the IP source address and IP destination address being the tunnel endpoints, and the IP protocol version number as 4. The srcrt'ed tunnel packets are more difficult to identify—they have the IP destination address as the tunnel destination endpoint address and an IP option set to LSRR(131) containing two recorded IP addresses, the first being the tunnel source endpoint and the second being the multicast destination group.

You now understand how most of the MBone packets appear. With this knowledge, you should be able to configure the filters on the routers appropriately. Note, however, that only the filter specifications for the encapsulated tunnels will be discussed, because they make up the majority of the tunnels on the MBone. Source routed tunnels have been outdated for a while and are completely being phased out.

Configuring the Firewall Filter

In figure 6.3, the MBone tunnel extends between the mrouter host on the internal subnet and another mrouter at the IP service provider's end. Let's designate the IP address of the tunnel endpoint within the local internal subnet as "IP.tnl_local," and IP address of tunnel endpoint at the remote end outside the firewall as "IP.tnl_remote." Now, in order to allow only IP multicast data and IGMP traffic to flow into or out of the internal subnet, the gateway machine will need to be configured. Using the tcpdump style expressions, discussed in a later section of this chapter, the IP multicast traffic that should be allowed through the firewall can be identified as follows:

```
(host IP.tnl_local and IP.tnl_remote) and (proto 2 or 4)
```

The traffic also can be broken down into outgoing and incoming data as:

```
(src IP.tnl_local and dst IP.tnl_remote) and (proto 2 or 4)
```

and

```
(src IP.tnl_remote and dst IP.tnl_local) and (proto 2 or 4)
```

Translating this tcpdump style expression directly into a router filter definition may not be possible. For Cisco Systems router software releases 10.0(1) and newer, the desired filter definitions may be expressed as the following:

```
access-list 101 permit 2 IP.tnl_remote 0.0.0.0 IP.tnl_local 0.0.0.0
access-list 101 permit 4 IP.tnl_remote 0.0.0.0 IP.tnl_local 0.0.0.0

access-list 102 permit 2 IP.tnl_local 0.0.0.0 IP.tnl_remote 0.0.0.0
access-list 102 permit 4 IP.tnl_local 0.0.0.0 IP.tnl_remote 0.0.0.0
```

Configuring the gateway machine and the router filter definitions as explained in the preceding will allow IP multicast traffic to flow over your MBone tunnel. Please check the router configuration system manual that was provided by your router vendor—the manual should go into more detail on configuring the router.

Security Analysis

Assuming a firewall filter utilizing the IP.tnl_local, IP.tnl_remote, and proto is possible, opening up the firewall still implies a level of trust with the remote tunnel provider. Authentication of any form for the packets that flow over the tunnel does not exist; therefore, any IP host can spoof itself as the remote tunnel endpoint, and hence be able to mount any kind of attack. This imposter would be free to send through the firewall any IP packets destined to the local tunnel endpoint and marked as IGMP or IP-in-IP. What security implications does this raise?

If the router filters do not allow fine grain specification of filtering requirements, then access to various kinds of network services is very limited. It may provide greater security to internal network resources, however—a higher level granularity in specifying filter specification enables you to keep a balance between levels of security versus easy access to network service.

Having learned how to install and configure your MBone connectivity in a secure manner, let's now take a look at how to manage, maintain, and monitor the network for IP multicast traffic. Several MBone and network monitoring and debugging tools are discussed in the next section. Note that most of these tools are designed and developed to run on Unix machines.

Debugging and Monitoring the MBone

Once the network systems administrator has set up and installed the MBone connectivity for your organization, the administrator's job is not completely over. The administrator should be prepared to allocate some time and resources that may be required if there is a need to reconfigure your outside tunnel(s) or the internal MBone setup, monitor the network traffic that flows over your local end of the MBone tunnel, or debug network problems. Unfortunately, there aren't any commercial software tools available to help administrators manage their MBone connectivity. There are, however, a few freely available tools on the Internet. Most of these tools help to debug MBone-related network problems and monitor MBone multimedia traffic at your end-host site or tunnel endpoint. A set of such software utilities is described in the following section.

Tcpdump

The tcpdump tool is a very versatile software package that enables system administrators to not only monitor and isolate MBone-related network problems, but also help with all different kinds of Internet traffic. Here, let's see how tcpdump relates to IP multicast traffic analysis and debugging. The latest version of tcpdump version 3.0.2 was mainly developed by Van Jacobson, Craig Leres, and Steve McCanne of Lawrence Berkeley Laboratory, the University of California, Berkeley. Tcpdump is available via anonymous FTP from the following:

```
ftp://ftp.ee.lbl.gov/tcpdump-3.0.2.tar.Z
```

Before you install this version of tcpdump at your site, you may want to take a look at the README file that is included in the software distribution. For a SunOS 4.1.x machine, installation of the tcpdump-3.0.2 may require installation of the packet capture utility libpcap version 0.0.6, which is available via anonymous FTP from:

```
ftp://ftp.ee.lbl.gov/libpcap.tar.Z
```

The installation of both libpcap and tcpdump is fairly easy—just follow the directions in the README files. Typing the following two commands in each directory may be sufficient:

```
% configure <return>
% make <return>
```

Tcpdump and libpcap have been built and tested under SGI Irix 4.x & 5.2, SunOS 4.x, Solaris 2.3, BSD/386 v1.1, DEC/OSF v1.3 v2.0, and Ultrix 4.x. SunOS 3.5, 4.3BSD Reno/ Tahoe, and 4.4BSD are supported as well.

If installed on a SunOS machine, you may have to log in as root before you can use the tcpdump program. Tcpdump prints out the headers of packets on a network interface that matches the boolean expression:

```
% tcpdump expression
```

Thus, to monitor IGMP traffic on your subnet, type the following:

```
% tcpdump ip proto igmp
```

To get a dump of the multicast traffic that comes over your MBone tunnel to your local subnet, type the following:

```
% tcpdump src <IP.tnl_remote>
```

Most other features and commands for tcpdump can be looked up in the help file (or the man page) that is bundled with the software distribution. You can also look up the man page by typing:

```
% nroff -man tcpdump.1 | more
```

Tcpdump program is very well covered and discussed in great detail in Stevens [4] (see bibliography).

Netstat

As the name suggests, netstat stands for *Network statistics tool*. It enables you to obtain IP multicast-related packet statistics. A few IP multicast-related options are mentioned in the following; however, netstat also facilitates collection of other Internet related traffic statistics.

- The "netstat -m" command recognizes four new multicast related mbuf types.
- The IGMP statistics are now included in the "netstat -s" command output, or explicitly with the command "netstat -p igmp."
- The "netstat -a" option may be used when printing interface information; for example, typing the command **netstat -nia** will print out all addresses (unicast and multicast) associated with each network interface, including link-level addresses. The only link-level addresses currently recognized are Ethernet addresses, and then only for some types of Ethernet interface (i.e., le).
- The "-M" option prints the kernel's multicast forwarding cache.
- The "-Ms" prints miscellaneous statistics related to multicast routing.

Before the "-p igmp" option will work, you must add the following line to the /etc/protocols:

```
igmp   2      IGMP         # internet group management protocol
```

Mrdebug

The mrdebug program is used to debug the multicast packet routing on the MBone. Mrdebug enables the user to display the multicast routes taken by a multicast message in a given network. The mrdebug program reads in the network topology and subnet descriptions from the files supplied to it. If given an IP source address for the multicast data stream, mrdebug then calculates the multicast tree. Mrdebug can display either the entire tree or the path from the IP source host to a particular destination host.

The format and contents of the subnet file and the topology file for mrdebug are described in detail in the help files included in the software distribution. This program was developed by Deborah Agarwal at Lawrence Berkeley Labs, and is available via anonymous FTP from `ftp://ftp.ee.lbl.gov/mrdebug.tar.Z`.

Note that the program will not run if not supplied with the topology and subnet files. The topology files can also be generated automatically via the mrmap program, described later in this chapter. The format of the file produced by the mrmap program is compatible with the topology file required for the mrdebug program.

This program can also be run interactively. The program asks the user different questions, and responds based on user's input. In the interactive mode, the user will be presented with the following commands on the screen:

```
Current source:
Current destination:
Enter command:
```

Typing '**?**' as a command will display all the command options supported. Detailed help on the mrdebug program is also available through the manual page that is included in the software distribution.

Multicast Ping

Packet Internet Groper (ping) is a standard utility for most TCP/IP implementations. The multicast-enabled ping software is available as part of the IP multicast kernel software distribution. The multicast ping software is included in the software distribution under the mrouted directory.

The modified ping provides control of the IP multicast transmission through the following new options:

- -l—inhibits multicast loopback.
- -t <ttl>—sets the multicast time-to-live to <ttl>.
- -i <addr>—sends multicasts from the interface with local address <addr>, given in a.b.c.d format.

This version of ping also supports the -R (record route) option.

Map-mbone

Map-mbone attempts to display the network topology of all the multicast routers that are reachable from any given multicast router on the MBone. If the IP address of the multicast router is not specified on the command line, then the map-mbone program assumes the default starting point for building the network topology as the local mrouter. To use this software, one must be logged in as root on your local host.

Map-mbone supports several other options as well. A manual help page is included as part of this freely available software on the Internet. Mrmap was developed by Pavel Curtis at Xerox PARC (Xerox Palo Alto Research Centre) Corp. An example displaying the use of this software is as follows:

```
#map-mbone collage.foo.com
192.50.58.17 (collage): <v2.2>
   192.50.58.17:  129.100.48.211 (morgul.mbone.net) [1/32/tunnel]
                  192.50.58.17 (collage) [1/1/querier]
```

Here, the map-mbone program was run on the host collage.foo.com. The program output shows that there is an MBone tunnel between the hosts collage.foo.com and morgul.mbone.net. The tunnel has the specifications of 1/32, meaning that the tunnel has the metric 1 and threshold 32. Also, the collage.foo.com multicast router is running version 2.2 of the mrouted program.

Rtpqual

Rtpqual is a simple multiprotocol multicast data (RTPv1) monitoring program. It allows end-hosts on the MBone to monitor the quality of the MBone multimedia data reception, especially if it is RTPv1-compliant. (RTPv1 stands for *Real-Time Protocol, version 1*.) The program understands the RTP protocol and listens for RTP messages, then computes and displays on the monitor statistics such as data packets received, lost data packets, percentage loss, late and out of sequence control packets arrived, the amount of data, and control bytes received by the end user site. In order to use this tool, you do not have to log in as root—it works fine with your normal user id.

The syntax to use rtpqual is the following:

```
Usage: rtpqual [<group> [<port> [<format>]]]
```

Rtpqual software is freely available on the Internet in binary form for the SunOS from `ftp://ftp.ee.lbl.gov/rtpqual` and in source form from `ftp://ftp.ee.lbl.gov/rtpqual.c`.

Mrmap

Mrmap is used to map all or a portion of a DVMRP-based multicast Internet backbone, such as the MBone. The program achieves this by doing a recursive, depth-first tree-walk starting at the IP address of the multicast router host specified by the administrator. The mrmap program can be used either by itself to determine the multicast topology, or in conjunction with the mrdebug program, discussed earlier, to determine multicast routes on the MBone. The basic syntax for using the program is as follows:

```
mrmap mrouter
```

Mrmap also supports a "-t" option, which is useful in cases where you want to limit the mapping to some smaller subset of the MBone. For example, the command:

```
mrmap -t 32 imr
```

where "imr" is some multicast router at some site on the Internet, would map only the multicast routers at that site, and not beyond. This assumes, however, that the site follows the MBone convention of putting a threshold of 32 at its boundary. Detailed capabilities of the tool are thoroughly discussed in the manual help page that is bundled with the software distribution. The software was written by Van Jacobson at the University of California at Berkeley, Lawrence Berkeley Labs, and is freely available via anonymous FTP from:

```
ftp://ftp.ee.lbl.gov/mrmap.tar.Z.
```

Mtrace

Assessing problems in the distribution of IP multicast traffic can be difficult. This tool helps in collecting statistics about the multimedia data traffic that flows over the MBone. It traces the branch of a multicast tree from a source to a receiver for a particular multicast group, and gives statistics about packet rates and losses for each hop along the path. It can be invoked in its simplistic mode as:

```
mtrace source
```

This will trace the route from the source host of multicast data traffic to the local host for a default IP multicast address. This command will yield only the route for the default IP multicast address, not the associated packet counts.

Mtrace supports several interesting powerful multicast routing-related debugging features, but their use requires version 3.3 or newer of the mrouted program. A more detailed list of capabilities of the mtrace software can be found in the help file included in the software distribution.

This software package was developed by Steve Casner of ISI and is available via anonymous FTP from `ftp://ftp.isi.edu/mbone/mtrace.tar.Z`. The program requires you to log in to the local host as root to use the tool. The distribution also contains a man page or the help file.

Mrinfo

Mrinfo displays information about a multicast router that is connected to the MBone. The information displayed consists of the version number of the mrouted program, how the mrouter is connected to other mrouters via tunnels, and the tunnel specifications. The mrouted information can be queried and viewed either for the local mrouter on your organization subnet or remote mrouters on the MBone. In its simple form, the mrouter information can be obtained by typing the following command while logged in as root:

```
mrinfo      <mrouter_name_or_address>
```

A sample program output from a local mrouter via the mrinfo program is shown in the following. Note that here the command is executed on the same machine as the local mrouter machine:

```
collage.foo.com# mrinfo collage.foo.com
192.50.58.17 (collage) [version 2.2]:
  192.50.58.17 -> 0.0.0.0 (local) [1/1/querier]
  192.50.58.17 -> 127.148.48.211 (morgul.mbone.net) [1/32/tunnel]
```

The following example shows how to query a remote mrouted host "morgul.mbone.net" from the local host "collage.foo.com."

```
collage.foo.com# mrinfo morgul.mbone.net
127.148.48.211 (morgul.mbone.net) [version 10.2]:
  127.148.48.211 -> 0.0.0.0 (local) [1/0/querier]
  127.148.48.211 -> 192.203.230.241 (mbone.asi.asa.gov) [1/0/tunnel]
  127.148.48.211 -> 130.119.244.11 (utumno.mbone.net) [1/0/tunnel]
  127.148.48.211 -> 191.216.188.11 (Angband.mbone.NET) [1/0/tunnel]
  127.148.48.211 -> 204.60.73.10 (Valinor.mbone.NET) [1/0/tunnel]
  127.148.48.211 -> 190.35.180.20 (mbone-seattle.newnet.net) [1/0/tunnel]
  127.148.48.211 -> 128.250.1.6 (mullala.ab.OZ.AU)[1/0/tunnel/disabled/down]
  127.148.48.211 -> 192.9.5.5 (play.ground.COM) [1/0/tunnel]
  127.148.48.211 -> 16.1.0.24 (nicotine.pa.com) [1/0/tunnel]
  127.148.48.211 -> 198.93.142.5 (s2ad1.global.net) [1/0/tunnel]
  127.148.48.211 -> 36.56.0.27 (Mighty.Dog.EDU) [1/0/tunnel]
  127.148.48.211 -> 192.48.153.6 (ene.GI.COM) [1/0/tunnel]
```

```
127.148.48.211 -> 192.50.58.17 (collage) [1/0/tunnel]
127.148.48.211 -> 131.20.254.59 (nps.marine.mil) [1/0/tunnel]
127.148.48.211 -> 127.14.134.160 (vault.cse.edu) [1/0/tunnel]
127.148.48.211 -> 17.255.4.30 (atg.banana.com) [1/0/tunnel]
127.148.48.211 -> 15.25.176.33 (matmos.hpl.com) [1/0/tunnel]
```

This example shows how the mrouted host "mrogul.mbone.net" is providing the IP multicast tunnels to other hosts on the MBone. These MBone hosts may or may not be on the same subnet as "mrogul.mbone.net." As you can see, "127.148.48.211" is the IP address of the mrouted host "morgul.mbone.net" and has MBone tunnels to 192.203.230.241 (mbone.asi.asa.gov), 130.119.244.11 (utumno.mbone.net), 191.216.188.11 (Angband.mbone.NET), and so on. The mrinfo program also detects and reports on the tunnels that are down (or turned off)—for example, the tunnel to 128.250.1.6 (mullala.ab.OZ.AU) [1/0/tunnel/disabled/down] is down and disabled. Disabling the tunnel is easy; it can be turned off at your end if you stop running the mrouting daemon "mrouted."

New Multimedia Transports and Operating Systems

Thus far in this book, you have seen how the MBone multimedia works. Clearly some functionalities have been added to the basic computing infrastructure by the computer manufacturers, operating system, and router vendors. You have also seen that most desktop computers now come factory built with IP-multicasting support, multimedia devices and drivers, and networking modems or Ethernet cards. This is a good start for doing multimedia internetworking. For this technology to go further, however, more advanced supporting features will be needed, such as the following:

- Reserving and allocating network bandwidth before multimedia movies are transmitted and received between various Internet hosts.
- Guarantees and *Quality of Service* (QoS) specifiers on multimedia data delivery over the Internet and the MBone.
- Better and faster compression and decompression of multimedia data.
- Better archiving of huge amounts of digital multimedia movies with fast I/O accesses.

And, of course, all of these features must be offered at an affordable price.

Work is already being done in this direction in the IETF working groups to design and implement some of the features mentioned in the preceding list. RTP is the real-time protocol that was recently designed by the IETF-AVT (*Audio Video Transport*) group. The *Resource Reservation Protocol* (RSVP) design work is already in progress. RSVP will enable computers and networks to work together to negotiate the issues mentioned in the first two bullets of the preceding list.

RTPv2: Real-Time Protocol

The *audio-video transport working group* (AVT WG) within the IETF was charged with developing a protocol that facilitates the transport of real-time data, such as interactive voice and video, over packet-switched networks such as the Internet. The working group now has finalized the *real-time transport protocol* (RTP) and an associated control protocol called RTCP. The final specifications draft for the design of the protocol has been submitted to the IESG Secretary for publication as Proposed Standard Internet RFC.

The RTP is an application transport protocol for transporting real-time interactive multimedia, such as the data generated in desktop multimedia conferencing. The design of the protocol, however, is not tied to any specific media like audio or video. RTP can potentially be used for designing different kinds of interactive applications that require time-critical delivery. Most software applications on the MBone today use the RTPv1 (version 1) and/or RTPv2 (version 2) protocol. Encoded multimedia data is compressed and embedded inside RTP protocol before delivery. RTCP provides lots of control functions for the multimedia data being transported in RTP.

The architecture for RTPv2-enabled applications is shown in figure 6.4.

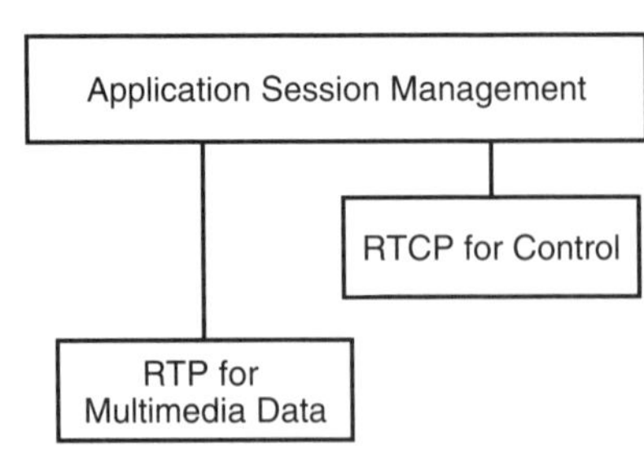

Figure 6.4

The RTP and RTCP application transport protocol stack.

As shown in figure 6.4, RTP carries the data, and RTCP carries the control information that reflects the quality of data being received by each participating host on the MBone. This control information allows applications in adapting to changing network traffic conditions. Session management functions are left to the application itself. Note that the RTP sessions are conducted over UDP/IP datagrams over the MBone when multihost communications are involved. Popular MBone software like VIC, Nevot, FTPVideo, and NV use the RTP protocol for transporting audio and video media across the MBone.

New Age Operating System Kernels and Routers

The *resource reservation setup protocol* (RSVP) is an Internet control protocol designed for an integrated services Internet. It is designed to run on top of the IP protocol. RSVP provides receiver-initiated setup of resource reservations for multicast or unicast data that flows over the Internet. This technology is being developed for the desktop computer operating systems, as well as for Internet routers.

Figure 6.5 shows that the RSVP capability will exist on computer desktops—as a result, the application software will be able to use the RSVP functionality in the operating system. Each host operating system will in turn be able to interact on the network with the RSVP, enabling IP routers to specify, reserve, and monitor network resources on the Internet and the MBone. Note that the figure also shows a traditional non-RSVP computer desktop, which implies that RSVP will work quite interoperably with both RSVP-enabled, as well as RSVP-deprived environments. It is an end-to-end solution.

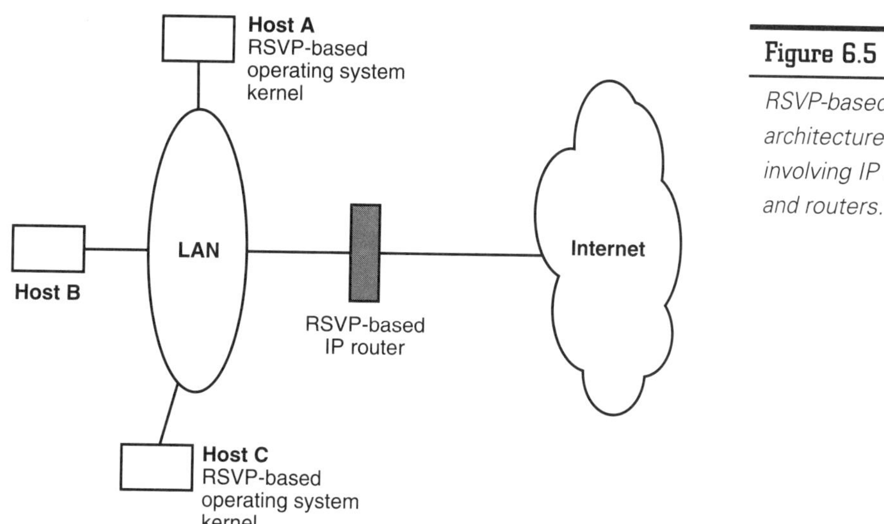

Figure 6.5

RSVP-based routing architecture involving IP hosts and routers.

The RSVP operates on top of IP, occupying the place of a transport protocol in the protocol stack. Like ICMP, IGMP, and routing protocols, however, RSVP does not transport application data, but is rather an Internet control protocol. RSVP is not itself a routing protocol—it sends RSVP messages to reserve resources along the delivery path(s) between a set of sources and the destinations of the multimedia data.

Thus, RSVP is an enabling technology for providing an integrated service-oriented environment on the Internet and the MBone. *Integrated service* means the capability that enables the operating system and the network to understand a set of QoS parameters specified by time-constraints on the media, and allocation of system resources such as CPU time or memory buffers for a multimedia data stream. As a result, the multimedia data stream is transported between multiple Internet sites and hosts with a guaranteed quality.

Writing Your First MBone Application

Now that you understand the underlying principles of MBone and IP multicasting, you are ready to develop your first sample application. In this example, you will learn how to send and receive IP multicast data over the MBone. You will use the BSD networking conventions because that is what is supported by Unix and Microsoft Windows 95 and Windows NT operating systems. It is assumed, however, that you are already familiar with developing TCP/IP networking applications using datagram sockets.

Operating System APIs

IP multicasting *Application Programming Interfaces* (APIs) are currently supported only on AF_INET sockets of type SOCK_DGRAM and SOCK_RAW, and only on subnetworks for which the interface driver has been modified to support multicasting. IP multicast support exists for Ethernet, FDDI, and ATM network interface drivers.

In this section, you first will examine some basic network API elements that have been recently introduced by your operating system. If you look at any MBone application, you will quite invariably see the use of the following API elements:

```
#include <netinet/in.h>

u_char ttl;
struct ip_mreq mreq;
struct sockaddr_in sin;

setsockopt(sock, IPPROTO_IP, IP_MULTICAST_TTL, &ttl, sizeof(ttl));
```

```
setsockopt(sock, IPPROTO_IP, IP_ADD_MEMBERSHIP, &mreq, sizeof(mreq));

setsockopt(sock, IPPROTO_IP, IP_DROP_MEMBERSHIP, &mreq, sizeof(mreq));

IN_CLASSD(sin.sin_addr.s_addr);
IN_MULTICAST (sin.sin_addr.s_addr);
```

The first line <netinet/in.h> is the header file that defines all the network parameters associated with IP multicast setsockopt() programming APIs. Therefore, this header file needs to be included in every multicasting application.

In earlier chapters, it was mentioned that an application has to be a member of a multicast address group before the application can receive IP multicast data from that address. The same need not apply, however, if the application wants to send datagrams to a multicast address group. Next, you will see how this is achieved in terms of programming.

Sending IP Multicast Data

A new socket option allows the TTL for multicast datagrams to be set to any value between 0 to 255, in order to control the scope of the multicasts:

```
u_char ttl;
setsockopt(sock, IPPROTO_IP, IP_MULTICAST_TTL, &ttl, sizeof(ttl));
```

Once the socket is configured, simply make the sendto () calls to the destination multicast address in order to multicast the application data.

Receiving IP Multicast Data

Before a host can receive IP multicast datagrams, it must become a member of one or more IP multicast groups. A process can ask the host to join a multicast group by using the following socket option:

```
struct ip_mreq mreq;

setsockopt(sock, IPPROTO_IP, IP_ADD_MEMBERSHIP, &mreq, sizeof(mreq))
```

This socket option call allows an Internet host to be added to the membership of a specific multicast group address. The "mreq" structure is defined in <netinet/in.h> file, as follows:

```
struct ip_mreq {
   struct in_addr imr_multiaddr;/* multicast group to join */
   struct in_addr imr_interface;/* interface to join on    */
 }
```

Once you decide to stop receiving multicast data from a specific multicast address, you may do so by dropping your membership to that group via the following socket option call:

```
setsockopt(sock, IPPROTO_IP, IP_DROP_MEMBERSHIP, &mreq, sizeof(mreq))
```

To receive multicast datagrams sent to a particular port, it is necessary to bind to that local port, leaving the local address unspecified (i.e. INADDR_ANY).

The API calls IN_CLASSD() or IN_MULTICAST () are helper functions that enable you to test if a given Internet address is a multicast address or not.

Chapter Summary

The MBone is still in a phase where the infrastructure is being upgraded so that IP multicasting becomes native to all IP routers. In such a case, MBone tunnels are not needed to get connected to the MBone. All IP routers will understand the class D multicast packets and route them like any other IP packet. Until then, the MBone remains a virtual network consisting of IP encapsulated tunnels. Connecting a subnet to the MBone is done via tunnels and with cooperation from your local MBone service provider. As you learned in this chapter, commercial vendors are fully behind this technology and are actively upgrading the computer hardware and software technology to support IP multicasting. Newer technologies like RTP and RSVP will truly make the MBone experience new age, because QoS and network resources will be guaranteed for a fair price.

In addition, network security is always an area of concern. Many Internet sites employ network firewalls to reduce exposure of internal resources, while still benefiting from limited Internet connectivity. Most current firewalls filter through IP addresses and port numbers to control communication between specific hosts and services; this is not sufficient for IP multicast tunnels. It is possible to easily identify IGMP DVMRP and encapsulated IP multicast packets exchanged between tunnel endpoints, and to translate this into appropriate filter specifications for placement on a firewall router. Security risks introduced by the multicast packet filters appear minimal, in any case.

p a r t

Appendixes

appendix A

MBone Resources on the Internet

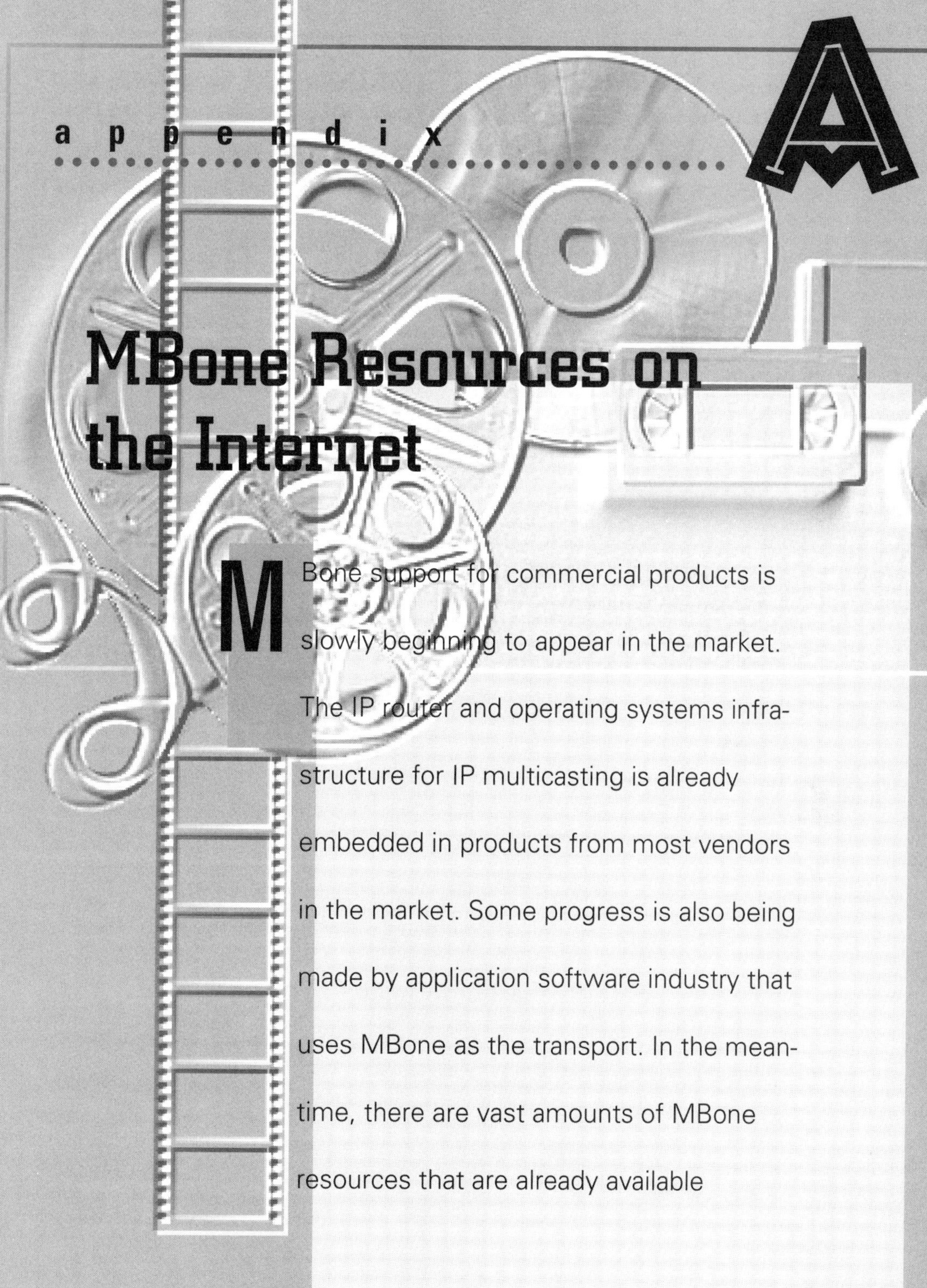

MBone support for commercial products is slowly beginning to appear in the market. The IP router and operating systems infrastructure for IP multicasting is already embedded in products from most vendors in the market. Some progress is also being made by application software industry that uses MBone as the transport. In the meantime, there are vast amounts of MBone resources that are already available free of charge on the Internet in the form of application software, technical information, and help information. This appendix contains a list of such readily accessible resources.

MBone Application Software

Several pieces of MBone application software were examined in Chapter 4, "MBone Multimedia Applications." Here is a comprehensive listing of such application software previously discussed, including how and where to find the software so it can be downloaded.

Session Directory

Session Directory (SD) is available via anonymous FTP. Just type the following on your workstation:

```
prince% ftp ftp.ee.lbl.gov (128.3.112.20)
prince% cd conferencing/sd/
prince% bin
prince% mget sd-*.tar.Z
```

To create a directory into which you can move the distribution, type the following:

```
prince% mkdir sd
prince% mv sd-*.tar.Z ./sd/.
prince% cd sd
prince% zcat sd-*.tar.Z | tar xvf -
```

This will install the contents of the distribution in this directory. The distribution contains the SD binary and a manual page as well.

Multimedia Conference Control

Multimedia Conference Control (MMCC) is available via anonymous FTP. Type the following commands on your workstation:

```
prince% ftp ftp.isi.edu (128.9.0.32)
prince% cd confctrl/mmcc/
prince% bin
prince% mget mmcc-*.tar.Z
```

To create a directory into which you can move the distribution, type the following:

```
prince% mkdir mmcc
prince% mv mmcc-*.tar.Z ./mmcc/.
prince% cd mmcc
prince% zcat mmcc-*.tar.Z | tar xvf -
```

This will install the contents of the distribution in this directory.

Mmphone

Mmphone is available via anonymous FTP. Type the following commands on your workstation:

```
prince% ftp ftp.eit.com (192.100.58.3)
prince% cd pub/share/
prince% bin
prince% mget wwwphone.*
```

To create a directory into which you can move the distribution, type the following:

```
prince% mkdir wwwphone
prince% mv wwwphone.* ./wwwphone/.
prince% cd wwwphone
prince% chmod +x *
```

Check `http://www.eit.com/software/mmphone/phoneform.html` for additional details.

CU-SeeMe

CU-SeeMe is available via anonymous FTP. Use your FTP tool to access the following FTP site:

```
prince% ftp gated.cornell.edu (132.236.199.65)
prince% cd pub/video
```

For the Mac version of the software, fetch the file Mac.CU-SeeMe0.*xxx*. Download the README file from that directory in text mode. Read it and obtain the other files you need.

For the Windows/PC version, fetch the file PC.CU-SeeMe W0.*xxx*. Download the README file from that directory in text mode and the cuseeme.zip file in binary mode.

A detailed updated README instruction file can also be fetched via the following FTP site:

```
ftp://k12.cnidr.org/pub/Mac/Dir-CUSeeMe/.
```

CU-SeeMe Reflector

The CU-SeeMe reflector sources and binaries are available via anonymous FTP. Type the following commands:

```
prince% ftp gated.cornell.edu (132.236.199.65)
prince% cd pub/video/Reflector/4.00b1.dist/
prince% bin
prince% mget reflect.*
```

The FTP site contains sources, as well as pre-compiled binaries for most Unix platforms. A sample copy of a reflector configuration file is also available at the same FTP site—the file is named "reflect.conf." A helper file called "README.reflector.4.00b1.txt" explains the different technical terms and jargons used in the reflector configuration file; therefore, it is a good idea to fetch this file and read it.

NetVideo

NetVideo (NV) is available via anonymous FTP. Just type the following on your workstation:

```
prince% ftp parcftp.xerox.com (13.1.64.94)
prince% cd pub/net-research/nv-3.3beta/
prince% bin
prince% mget nvbin-*.tar.Z
```

To create a directory into which you can move the distribution, type the following:

```
prince% mkdir nv
prince% mv nvbin-*.tar.Z ./nv/.
prince% cd nv
prince% zcat nvbin-*.tar.Z | tar xvf -
```

This will install the contents of the distribution in this directory. To get the sources, get the file nvsrc.tar.Z.

Video Conference Tool

Video Conference Tool (VIC) is available via anonymous FTP. Just type the following on your workstation:

```
prince% ftp ftp.ee.lbl.gov (128.3.112.20)
prince% cd conferencing/vic/
prince% bin
prince% mget vic-*.tar.Z
```

To create a directory into which you can move the distribution, type the following:

```
prince% mkdir vic
prince% mv vic-*.tar.Z ./sd/.
prince% cd vic
prince% zcat vic-*.tar.Z | tar xvf -
```

This will install the contents of the distribution in this directory.

To build VIC from source, simply run the ./configure script in the top-level of the distribution directory, and then run "make." You'll need to have tcl/tk (v7.3/3.6) installed (or built in the directory above the VIC tree), and the "BLT" library (v1.7), available via anonymous FTP to `ftp.aud.alcatel.com`, in the directory tcl/extensions.

INRIA Videoconferencing System

INRIA Videoconferencing System (IVS) has a Web-based home page of its own, and it is available at the following:

```
http://zenon.inria.fr:8003/rodeo/personnel/Thierry.Turletti/ivs.html
```

IVS is available via anonymous FTP. Type the following commands on your workstation:

```
prince% ftp zenon.inria.fr (138.96.32.21)
prince% cd rodeo/ivs/version3.5/
prince% bin
prince% mget ivs3.5-*.tar.Z
```

To create a directory into which you can move the distribution, type the following:

```
prince% mkdir ivs
prince% mv ivs3.5-*.tar.Z ./ivs/.
prince% cd ivs
prince% zcat ivs3.5-*.tar.Z | tar xvf -
```

This will install the contents of the distribution in this directory.

Visual Audio Tool

Visual Audio Tool (VAT) is available via anonymous FTP. Type the following commands on your workstation:

```
prince% ftp ftp.ee.lbl.gov (128.3.112.20)
prince% cd conferencing/vat/
prince% bin
prince% mget vat-*.tar.Z
```

To create a directory into which you can move the distribution, type the following:

```
prince% mkdir vat
prince% mv vat-*.tar.Z ./vat/.
prince% cd vat
prince% zcat vat-*.tar.Z | tar xvf -
```

This will install the contents of the distribution in this directory. The distribution contains the VAT binary and a manual page as well.

Network Voice Terminal

Network Voice Terminal (Nevot) is available via anonymous FTP. Type the following commands on your workstation:

```
prince% ftp gaia.cs.umass.edu (128.119.40.186)
prince% cd pub/hgschulz/nevot/
prince% bin
prince% mget nevot-3.*.tar.Z
```

To create a directory into which you can move the distribution, type the following:

```
prince% mkdir nevot
prince% mv nevot-3.*.tar.Z ./nevot/.
prince% cd nevot
prince% zcat nevot-3.*.tar.Z | tar xvf -
```

This will install the contents of the distribution in this directory. The distribution contains a Nevot binary and a manual page as well.

MAVEN

MAVEN is available via anonymous FTP. Use your Mac FTP tool to access the following FTP site by typing the commands:

```
prince% ftp k12.cnidr.org
prince% cd pub/Mac/Dir-Soundstuff/
prince% bin
prince% get Maven-*.sea.bin
```

This will install the contents of the distribution in this directory.

Shared Mosaic

Shared Mosaic is available via anonymous FTP. Type the following commands on your workstation:

```
prince% ftp ftp.eit.com (192.100.58.3)
prince% cd pub/share/mosaic/beta/
prince% bin
prince% mget Shared-Mosaic-*.tar.Z
```

To create a directory into which you can move the distribution, type the following:

```
prince% mkdir smosaic
prince% mv Shared-Mosaic-*.tar.Z ./smosaic/.
prince% cd smosaic
prince% zcat Shared-Mosaic-*.tar.Z | tar xvf -
```

This will install the contents of the distribution in this directory. Once you start the program, you will see the built-in help system in the top menu bar as a pull-down menu.

WhiteBoard

WhiteBoard (WB) is available via anonymous FTP. Just type the following on your workstation:

```
prince% ftp ftp.ee.lbl.gov (128.3.112.20)
prince% cd conferencing/wb/
prince% bin
prince% mget wb-*.tar.Z
```

To create a directory into which you can move the distribution, type the following:

```
prince% mkdir wb
prince% mv wb-*.tar.Z ./wb/.
prince% cd wb
prince% zcat wb-*.tar.Z | tar xvf -
```

This will install the contents of the distribution in this directory. The distribution contains a WB binary and a help manual page.

IMM

IMM is available via anonymous FTP. Type the following commands on your workstation:

```
prince% ftp ftp.hawaii.edu (128.171.44.70)
prince% cd paccom/imm-3.3/
prince% bin
prince% mget imm.*.tar.Z
```

To create a directory into which you can move the distribution, type the following:

```
prince% mkdir imm
prince% mv imm.*.tar.Z ./imm/.
prince% cd imm
prince% zcat imm.*.tar.Z ¦ tar xvf -
```

This will install the contents of the distribution in this directory.

MBone Operating System Software

In Chapter 6, you learned how to install and configure MBone at your site within your subnet. Such installation may—but not always—require patching your operating system kernel with IP multicast extensions for the TCP/IP stack. Such IP multicast kernel extensions are freely available via anonymous FTP. This section contains a comprehensive list of the major FTP sites where you can get appropriate kernel software for your computing platform.

IP Multicast Kernel Patches for SunOS 4.1+

Version 3.5+ of the IP multicast operating system kernel patches is available at the following sites:

```
ftp://parcftp.xerox.com/pub/net-research/ipmulti/ipmulti3.5-sunos41x.tar.Z
ftp://ftp.adelaide.edu.au/pub/av/multicast/ipmulti3.5-sunos41x.tar.Z
ftp://ftp.ucs.ed.ac.uk/pub/videoconference/ipmulticast/ipmulti3.5-sunos41x.tar.Z
```

IP Multicast Kernel Patches for Solaris 2.3+

For Solaris 2.3+ machines, version 3.4+ of IP multicast kernel fixes and mrouter is available at the following:

`ftp://playground.sun.com/pub/multicast/`

IP Multicast Kernel Patches for Other Unix Operating Systems

For SGI running IRIX5.3+, version 3.3+ of the IP multicast kernel patches and mrouter is available at the following site:

`ftp://ftp.sgi.com/sgi/ipmcast/IRIX5/5.3/`

For DEC running OSF V2+ or Digital Unix Operating Systems, version 3.3+ of the IP multicast kernel patches and mrouter is available at:

`ftp://chocolate.pa.dec.com/mbone/`

and

`ftp://chocolate.pa.dec.com/mbone/HEADER.html`

For Intel PCs running Linux, most of the IP multicasting-related information is available at the following:

`http://andrew.triumf.ca/pub/linux/multicast-FAQ`

MBone Debugging Software

As discussed in Chapter 6, there are a few freely available software tools that enable system and network administrators to monitor, manage, and debug their MBone tunnels and service. This section contains a comprehensive list of all such tools.

Tcpdump

Tcpdump is available via anonymous FTP at the following site:

`ftp://ftp.ee.lbl.gov/tcpdump-3.0.2.tar.Z`

Before you install this version of tcpdump at your site, you may want to take a look at the README file that is included in the distribution. For a SunOS 4.1.x machine, installation of tcpdump-3.0.2 may require installation of the packet capture utility, libpcap version 0.0.6, which is available via anonymous FTP at:

```
ftp://ftp.ee.lbl.gov/libpcap.tar.Z
```

Once downloaded and saved, uncompress and untar the distribution via the following command:

```
% zcat libpcap.tar.Z | tar xvf -
% zcat tcpdump-3.0.2.tar.Z | tar svf -
```

Mtrace

This software package is available via anonymous FTP from the following:

```
ftp://ftp.isi.edu/mbone/mtrace.tar.Z.
```

Once downloaded and saved as mtrace.tar.Z, you can uncompress and untar the distribution via the following command:

```
% zcat mtrace.tar.Z | tar xvf -
```

Mrmap

Mrmap is available via anonymous FTP from the following site:

```
ftp://ftp.ee.lbl.gov/mrmap.tar.Z
```

Once downloaded and saved as mrmap.tar.Z, you can uncompress and untar the distribution via the following command:

```
% zcat mrmap.tar.Z | tar xvf -
```

Rtpqual

Rtpqual is available in binary form for the SunOS from **ftp://ftp.ee.lbl.gov/rtpqual** and in source form from **ftp://ftp.ee.lbl.gov/rtpqual.c**.

Map-Mbone

Map-mbone is available via anonymous FTP from the following site:

```
ftp://parcftp.xerox.com/pub/net-research/
```

Once downloaded and saved as map-mbone.tar.Z, you can uncompress and untar the distribution via the following command:

```
% zcat map-mbone.tar.Z | tar xvf -
```

Mrdebug

Mrdebug is available via anonymous FTP from:

```
ftp://ftp.ee.lbl.gov/mrdebug.tar.Z
```

Once downloaded and saved as mrdebug.tar.Z, you can uncompress and untar the distribution via the following command:

```
% zcat mrdebug.tar.Z | tar xvf -
```

MBone Online Information

In addition to software, there are other pieces of interesting information about the MBone that have been put online on the Internet and that are accessible via the Web. A few of these sites are listed in this section.

MBone Agenda Information

For most events on the MBone, it is a customary practice followed by organizers of such events to add a copy of the event schedule at this Web site. A copy of the MBone agenda and schedules can be browsed at this site via the following:

```
http://www.cilea.it/MBone/browse.html
```

To book a time slot for transmitting over the MBone, use:

```
http://www.cilea.it/MBone/book.html
```

Global MBone Home Page

This site gives an overview of the Global MBone and other relevant MBone information sites worldwide. Access it via the following:

```
http://www.mbone.com/techinfo/mbone/
```

Apple Corp.'s Information Site

Macintosh OpenTransport replaces Apple Corp.'s earlier MacTCP stack. Documentation on IP multicasting support, as well as the TCP/IP API, is available via anonymous FTP, as follows:

```
% ftp seeding.apple.com
% Name: anonymous
% password: <login_name@org_name.com>
ftp>cd /ess/public/opentransport/OT_Docs_textonly/
ftp>get OT_TCPIP
```

You can also type the following URL on your Web browser:

ftp://seeding.apple.com/ess/public/opentransport/OT_Docs_textonly/

Microsoft Corp.'s Information Site

Microsoft Corp.'s support for IP multicasting in Windows NT and Windows 95 is available from their anonymous FTP site, as follows:

```
% ftp ftp.microsoft.com
% Name: anonymous
% password: <login_name@org_name.com>
ftp>cd /bussys/WinSock/ms-ext/
ftp>bin
ftp>get MULTICAST.TXT
```

You can also type the following URL on your Web browser:

ftp://ftp.microsoft.com/bussys/WinSock/ms-ext/

appendix

B

The MBone Products Shopping Guide

The commercialization of various aspects of the MBone started a few years ago when operating system and IP router vendor companies released products based on IP multicasting technologies. Today, a host of IP router companies and operating system companies do sell products that enable MBone applications on the desktop. Only a handful of companies exist, however, that market MBone-based applications for end user desktop. This appendix contains a comprehensive listing of companies that sell products that facilitate use of the MBone.

The MBone IP Router Shopper's Guide

The Internet routers are a major part of the MBone data traffic management. Most of the multicast routers are free public domain routers that use tunneling as a way to route MBone traffic. In the long run, however, all the IP routers will be upgraded to support IP multicast routing natively. The following is a list of companies that are marketing routers that enable MBone traffic routing in native mode.

ALANTEC Corporation, California, USA

Product Name: PowerHub
Supports: DVMRP-based multicast routing support only
Contact: Alantec Corp., North America/Western Region
2115 O'Nel Drive
San Jose, CA 95131
Phone: 408-955-9000
Voice: 1-800-ALANTEC, 1-408-955-9000 outside the U.S.
E-mail: `powerhub@alantec.com`

Proteon, Inc., Massachusetts, USA

Product Name: CNX 500+, DNX 350, RBX 200
Supports: MOSPF and DVMRP support
Voice: 1-800-545-7464

Cisco Systems, Inc., California, USA

Product Name: Cisco 7000, Cisco 7500
Supports: PIM and DVMRP-based multicast routing support
Contact: Cisco Systems, Inc., Corporate Headquarters
170 West Tasman Drive
San Jose, CA 95134-1706
Phone: 408-526-4000
For sales assistance or product information in the U.S., please call 800-859-2726.

3Com Corporation, California, USA

Product Name: NETBuilder II, Beta in Sept.'95
Supports: DVMRP (3.5/3.6), MOSPF, IGMPv2 routing support
Contact: 3Com Corp.
5400 Bayfront Plaza
P.O. Box 58145
Santa Clara, CA 95052-8145
Voice: 408-764-5000

Bay Networks, Inc., USA

Bay Networks, Inc.
Corporate Headquarters
4401 Great America Parkway
Santa Clara, CA 95054
Voice: 1-800-8BAYNET

Agile Networks, Inc., USA

Product Name: ATMizer ATM and Ethernet Switch
Contact: Agile Networks Inc.
1300 Massachusetts Ave.
Boxborough, MA 01719
Voice: 1-800-ATM-XLAN

The MBone Operating System Shopper's Guide

As mentioned earlier, a lot of operating systems today do support IP multicasting in their kernel. Here is such a list of companies and operating systems that are available in the market.

Apple Corp., California, USA

Product Name: MacOS 7.5.2+, Mac OpenTransport
Supports: IP multicasting in the OS, IGMPv2
More info: Apple's IP multicasting support, as well as the TCP/IP API, is available via anonymous FTP:

```
ftp://seeding.apple.com/ess/public/opentransport/
OT_Docs_textonly/
```

Contact: Apple Computer Inc., Corporate Headquarters
One Infinite Loop
Cupertino, CA 95014
Voice: 1-408-996-1010

Microsoft Corp., Washington, USA

Product Name: Windows 95, Windows NT
Supports: IP multicasting, IGMPv1 on PC/MS-Windows platform
More info: available via their anonymous FTP site:

```
ftp://ftp.microsoft.com/bussys/WinSock/ms-ext/
```

FTP Software, Inc., Massachusetts, USA

Product Name: OnNet for Windows 2.1
Supports: IGMPv2 on PC/MS-Windows platform
Contact: FTP Software, Inc.
100 Brickstone Square, Fifth Floor
Andover, MA 01810
Voice: 1-800-282-4FTP, +1-508-685-3300

Trumpet Software International, Australia

Product Name: Trumpet Winsock, Version 2.1
Supports: Multicast support, but not sure what version of IGMP is supported. Check with the vendor.
Contact: Trumpet Software International Pty Ltd
GPO Box 1649
Hobart Tasmania 7001, Australia
Voice: +61-02-450220 (International)
E-mail (general): `info@trumpet.com.au`
E-mail (sales): `sales@trumpet.com.au`

Sun Microsystems Corp., California, USA

Product Name: Solaris 2.3+
Supports: IGMPv2
Contact: Local Sun Microsystems resellers

Silicon Graphics, Inc., California, USA

Product Name: IRIX 5.2+
Supports: IGMPv2
Contact: Local SGI workstation resellers

Digital Equipment Corp., USA

Product Name: OSF V2.0+, Digital Unix
Supports: IGMPv2
Contact: Local DEC workstation resellers

Multimedia Hardware Shopper's Guide

As you have seen, MBone multimedia does require a multimedia computer on your desktop. If your computer does not have the audio and video capabilities, then the following list may help you find the right hardware for your computer.

Vigra Inc., California, USA

Product name: VigraPix video card.
Supports: SUN workstations, SBus card, NTSC, PAL video inputs, NV video compression
More info: `http://www.vigra.com/`
Contact: VigraPix Inc.
10052 Mesa Ridge Court
San Diego, CA 92121
Voice: +1-619-597-7080, 1-800-66-VIGRA
E-mail: `sales@vigra.com`

Parallax Graphics, Inc., California, USA

Product Name: PowerVideo video card, MultiVideo card
Supports: SUN and HP workstations, SBus card, NTSC, PAL video input and output, JPEG video compression
More info: `http://www.parallax.com/`
Contact: Parallax Graphics, Inc.
2500 Condensa Street
Santa Clara, CA 95051
Voice: +1-408-727-2220
E-mail: `info@parallax.com`

Digital Equipment Corp., Massachusetts, USA

Product Name: DEC J300 Sound and Video Card
Supports: DEC Alpha workstations, NTSC, PAL video input and output, JPEG video compression, 8-bit/16-bit audio, 8 KHz, 11.025 KHz, 16 KHz, 22.05 KHz, 32 KHz, 44.1 KHz, 48 KHz sampling, ADPCM and GSM voice compression
More info: `ftp://ftp.digital.com/pub/Digital/info/infosheet/EC-F4364-10.txt`

Sun MicroSystems, Inc., California, USA

Product Name: SunVideo card
Supports: Sun workstations, SBus card, NTSC, PAL video inputs, JPEG, MPEG-1, CellB video compression
More info: `http://www.sun.com/smi/bang/SunVideo.html`
Contact: Local Sun reseller

Sun MicroSystems, Inc., California, USA

Product Name: Sun VideoPix Card
Supports: Sun workstations, SBus card, NTSC, PAL inputs; no video compression support
More info: `ftp://playground.sun.com under/pub/videopix/`

Silicon Graphics, Inc., California, USA

Product Name: Indigo Video Card
Supports: SGI workstations
More info: `http://www.sgi.com/`
Contact: Local SGI resellers

Hewlett Packard, Inc., California, USA

Product Name: MediaMagic 700 video card
Supports: HP workstations.
More info: `http://www.hp.com/`
Contact: Local HP reseller

Advanced Gravis Computer Technology, Canada

Product Name: GUS UltraMax, version 3.4, sound card
Supported: PC/Windows, 16-bit audio up to 48 KHz ADPCM, mu-law and a-law voice compression, full-duplex audio card
Cost: Approximately $200.00 (U.S.)
Contact: Advanced Graphics Computer Technology
111-7400 MacPherson Avenue
Burnaby, BC, Canada
Voice: +1-604-431-5020
E-mail: `tech@gravis.com`

Adlib Multimedia, Inc., Canada

Product Name: AdLib Gold 1000 sound card
Supports: PC/Windows
Contact: AdLib Multimedia
220 Grande Allee East, Suite 850
Quebec, QC, Canada
Voice: 1-800-463-2686, +1-418-529-9676

Creative Labs, California, USA

Product Name: Sound Blaster 16 sound hardware.
Supports: PC/Windows, 8-bit/16-bit audio I/O support ADPCM compression.
Contact: Creative Labs
2050 Duane Avenue
Santa Clara, CA 95054
Voice: +1-408-428-660

Media Vision, Inc., California, USA

Product Name: Pro AudioSpectrum 16
Supports: PC/Windows, 16-bit audio and 44 KHz sampling
Contact: Media Vision Inc.
47221 Fremont Blvd.
Fremont, CA 94539
Voice: 1-800-845-5870

Turtle Beach Systems, Inc., USA

Product Name: Multisound sound card
Supports: PC/Windows, 16-bit/8-bit audio resolution, 44.1 KHz, 22.05 KHz, 11.025 KHz
Contact: Turtle Beach Systems Inc.
Cyber Center, Unit 33
1600 Pennsylvania Ave.
York, PA 17404
Voice: +1-717-843-6916

Digital Vision, Inc., USA

Product Name: ComputerEyes/RT, TelevEyes video card
Supports: Macintosh computers
Contact info: Digital Vision Inc.
270 Bridge Street
Dedham, MA 02026
Voice: +1-617-329-5400
E-mail: `digvis@tiac.net`

micro Computer Products, Inc., USA

Product Name: microVideo DC1 TV video card
Supports: Macintosh computers
Contact info: micro Computer Products Inc.

Orchid Technology, Inc., USA

Product Name: Orchid Videola Pro/D video card
Contact: Orchid Technology Inc.
Voice: +1-510-683-0327

Creative Labs, Inc., USA

Product Name: VideoBlaster
Supports: PC/Windows, basic video in a window display
Contact: Creative Labs Inc.
1901 McCarthy Blvd.
Milpitas, CA 95035
Voice: +1-408-428-6600

Connectix Corp., USA

Product name: QuickCam video camera
Supports: Macintosh computers, grayscale video, no video card needed, uses serial port
Contact: Call MacConnection at 800-800-0002 (SKU #16287),MacWarehouse at 800-255-6227 (SKU #INP0397), or Mac Mall at 800-222-2808 (SKU #65746). QuickCam is also available through Tiger Software, CompUSA, Egghead Software, Computerware, Computer City, and Fry's.

VideoLabs, Inc., USA

Product Name: FlexCam video camera
Supports: All video hardware that takes NTSC/PAL input
Contact: VideoLabs Inc.

Guide to the MBone Service Providers

The MBone service provider companies are typically IP service provider companies. They help you set up your MBone tunnel, and in the configuration of the multicast routers. See table 5.2 in Chapter 5 for a list of MBone service providers on the Internet that you may find useful.

An updated list of such MBone service providers is maintained by Matt Mathis, and is available at the following:

```
http://www.psc.edu/~mathis/contacts.html
```

A separate list of MBone service providers in Europe is available at:

```
ftp://ftp.nic.surfnet.nl/surfnet/net-management/mbone/eu-contacts.txt
```

or

```
http://www.cs.ucl.ac.uk/mice/
```

For Japan, the MBone service contacts are:

Tokuda & Murai Laboratory
Keio University, Japan
Hiroyuki Kusumoto
+81-466-49-1090
kusumoto@wide.ad.jp

Nippon Telephone and Telegraph (NTT)
Hitoaki Sakamoto
hitoaki@mahler.ntt.jp

The MBone Application Software Shopper's Guide

The MBone applications that are being used today on the Internet are research prototypes—none of them are commercially supported. A few companies have just begun to appear in the market to take on the challenge of building and supporting the MBone desktop applications. These companies are listed as follows.

MCast Communications, Inc., USA

Product Name: MCast Server and other MBone software applications
Supports: Unix servers and Windows clients
Contact: MCast Communications Inc.
108 B East Middlefield Road
Mountain View, CA 94043
Voice: +1-415-964-4009
E-mail: info@mbone.com
URL: http://www.mbone.com/

White Pine Software, USA

Product Name: CU-SeeMe videoconferencing tool
Supports: Macintosh, PC/Windows computers, point-to-point scheme for video conferencing
Contact: White Pine Software, Inc.
1485 Saratoga Ave.
San Jose, CA 95129-4923
Voice: +1-408-446-1919

appendix

C

Internet Graphics and Video Formats

Multimedia can be stand-alone or networked. In stand-alone mode, the media flows only within one desktop between the HD, CD-ROM, memory, and display. MBone multimedia is an example of networked multimedia. This appendix is a compilation of multimedia (audio, video, graphics) formats and file types commonly used in stand-alone mode.

Table C.1

Desktop Media File Formats

Media File Formats	File Extensions
Adobe Illustrator	.AI
Algor	.BTM
Amiga Interchange Format	.IFF
AutoCAD	.DXF
Autodesk Animator Studio	.FLI
Autodesk Animator Studio	.FLC
Bitmapped Graphics	.BMP
Bitmapped Graphics	.PCX
Computer Graphics Metafile	.CGM
Director Animation	.MMM
Encapsulated PostScript	.EPS
Graphics Interchange Format	.GIF
Harvard Graphics Chart	.CHT
Hewlett Packard Graphics Language	.PLT
HyperText Markup Language	.HTML
IBM PIF	.PIF
M-Motion Video	.VID
MAC	.PCT
Microsoft Paint	.MSP
Microsoft Video for Windows	.AVI
Rich Text Format	.RTF
SGI Audio File	.AIFF
Special Generalized Markup Language	.SGML
SUN Audio File	.AU

Media File Formats	File Extensions
Tagged Image File Format	.TIF
Truevision TARGA	.TGA
Windows Metafile	.WMF

The following is a compilation of commonly used multimedia standards over the MBone in an internetworked environment.

Table C.1

Real-Time MBone Media Formats

Media Type	Media Sub-Type	Format
Audio	PCM	Pulse Code Modulation
	ADPCM	Adaptive Pulse Code Modulation
	LPC	Linear Predictive Coding
	GSM	General Special Mobile
	IDVI	Intel DVI
Video	NV	NetVideo
	CUSM	CU-SeeMe
	H.261	ITU, H.261
	JPEG	Joint Photographic Experts Group
	MPEG	Motion Picture Experts Group
	CellB	Sun CellB
	Indeo	Intel Indeo Video

appendix

D

MBone-Related Publications

The trade magazines mentioned in this appendix are mainly focused on commercial activities, such as new product and technology launches that are happening around the world in the field of Information Technologies (IT). Most of the coverage is focused at the Internet, TCP/IP, multimedia, desktop video, and networking-related product companies and their wares. Subscriptions to most of these magazines are free; however, you may be required to fill out a subscription form. Contact the appropriate sites mentioned in the following to see how to get the subscription form.

1. *InfoWorld Magazine*. For information:
   Voice: +1 800 227 8365, +1 415 572 7341
   URL: `http://www.infoworld.com/`

2. *LAN TIMES Magazine*. For information:
   Voice: +1 415 513 6800
   E-mail: `susan_briedenbach@wcmh.com`

3. *Interactive Week Magazine*, Ziff Davis Publishing. For more information:
   URL: `http://www.interactive-week.com/`

4. *Communications Week Magazine*

5. *Videomaker Magazine*, for audio/video equipment enthusiasts. For information:
   Voice: +1 619 745 2809
   URL: `http://www.videomaker.com/`

6. *Interactive Age Magazine*, a CMP publication. For information:
   Voice: +1 516 562 7383
   URL: `http://techweb.cmp.com/ia/`

7. *Computer Video Magazine*, JRS Publishing. For information:
   Voice: +1 703 998 7600.

8. *MicroPublishing News*, Micro Publishing Press. For information:
   Voice: +1 310 371 5787
   E-mail: `mpn@designlink.com`

9. *PC Magazine*, Ziff Davis Publishing. For information:
   Voice: +1 212-503-5100
   URL: `http://www.zdnet.com/~pcmag/`

10. *PC Week*, Ziff Davis Publishing. For information:
    URL: `http://www.zdnet.com/~pcweek/`

11. A Video Montage Publishing, Inc.
    701 Westchester Blvd.
    White Plains, NY 10604

12. New Media
    901 Mariner's Island Blvd.
    San Mateo, CA 94404

13. *Computer Artist*, PennWell Publishing Company
    One Technology Park Drive
    P.O. Box 987
    Westford, MA 01886
14. *Video Magazine*, Reese Communications, Inc.
    460 W. 34th Street
    New York, NY 10001
15. *Computer Graphics*, World PennWell Publishing Company
    One Technology Park Drive
    P.O. Box 987
    Westford, MA 01886
16. *Desktop Video*
    TechMedia Publishing, Inc.
    80 Elm Street
    Peterborough, NH 03458

appendix E

The Reflector Sites

As you saw earlier in the book, CU-SeeMe software was primarily designed to do only point-to-point video conferencing over the Internet. CU-SeeMe works around this limitation, however, by using reflector sites to do multiparty video sessions. The following is a compiled list of active reflector sites to which CU-SeeMe users could potentially connect.

Site: Australia
IP Host: reflect.adelaide.edu.au
alias: (Australia) Adelaide 129.127.12.42 s r

Site: Australia
IP Host: 203.2.239.3
alias: (Australia) Geko 203.2.239.3 s r

Site: Australia, Murdoch University
IP Host: cleo.murdoch.edu.au
alias: (Australia) Murdoch Univ. 134.115.224.60 s r
Special Note: Keep your cap (bandwidth) at 80 Kbps max. Connection to reflector by appointment only. For further information:

`http://134.115.224.48/`
Geoff Rehn, e-mail: `rehn@cleo.murdoch.edu.au`

Site: University of Queensland, Australia
IP Host: psy.uq.oz.au
alias: (Australia) Psy 130.102.32.1 s r

Site: Australia
IP Host: reflector.rmit.edu.au
alias: (Australia) RMIT 131.170.9.1 s r

Site: The University of Melbourne, Australia
IP Host: reflector.unimelb.edu.au
alias: (Australia) Univ. of Melbourne 128.250.20.187 s r
Special Note: Casual use welcome at 80 Kbps max. Connection to the reflector for conferencing purposes by appointment only. For further information:

`http://www.unimelb.edu.au/`
Martin Gleeson, e-mail: `gleeson@unimelb.edu.au`
12 Dec 94, gleeson

Site: University of Queensland, Australia
IP Host: clix.aarnet.edu.au
alias: (Australia) Univ. Queensland 130.102.128.59 s r

Site: AI-Lab Vrije Universiteit, Brussel, Belgium
IP Host: arti.vub.ac.be
alias: (Belgium) Vrije Univ. AI-Lab 134.184.26.10 s r

Special Note: The reflector's primary use is the transmission of seminars and live scientific experiments. For further information:

`http://arti.vub.ac.be/welcome.html`
Peter Stuer, e-mail: `peterst@arti.vub.ac.be`

Site: Catholic University of Rio de Janeiro, Brazil
IP Host: oxala.inf.puc-rio.br
alias: (Brazil) PUC-Rio 139.82.17.20 s r
Special Note: 80 Kbps max bandwidth use. Feel free to use anytime. For further information:

`http://www.inf.puc-rio.br/`
Hugo Fuks, e-mail: `hugo@inf.puc-rio.br`

Site: University of Sao Paulo, Brazil
IP Host: suncisc.cisc.sc.usp.br
alias: (Brazil) Univ. Sao Paulo 143.107.225.6 s r

Site: Dalhousie University, Nova Scotia, Canada
IP Host: sparky.ucis.dal.ca
alias: (Canada) Dalhousie Univ. 129.173.2.56 s r
Special Note: Maximum bandwidth use 80 Kbps. For further information:

`http://www.dal.ca/`
Vivien Hannon, e-mail: `Vivien.Hannon@Dal.CA`

Site: University of Manitoba, Department of ECE, Canada
IP Host: kinsner2.ee.umanitoba.ca
alias: (Canada) Univ. Manitoba 130.179.8.44 s r
Special Note: Contact information:

W. Kinsner, e-mail: `kinsner@ee.umanitoba.ca`

Site: University of Vaasa, Vaasa, Finland
IP Host: zippo.uwasa.fi
alias: (Finland) Univ. Vaasa 193.166.120.3 s r
Special Note: Try day and evening (Finnish time +2 GMT). For further information:

`http://www.uwasa.fi/`
Tuomas Eerola, e-mail: `te@uwasa.fi`

Site: Telecomm "Grande Ecole," Brittany, France
IP Host: 130.190.6.28
alias: (France) Telecomm Grand Ecole 130.190.6.28 s r

Site: Radio HK
IP Host: 204.119.173.22
alias: (HK) Radio HK 204.119.173.22 s r
Special Note: Audio-only, receive-only. 24 hours a day, 7 days a week. For further information:

`http://hkweb.com/radio/`
Norman Hajjar, e-mail: `norman_hajjar@hk.com`

Site: Rotterdam School of Mgmt, Rotterdam, Holland
IP Host: reflector.fbk.eur.nl
alias: (Holland) Rotterdam Mgmt. 130.115.150.2 s r
Special Note: For further information:

Wetering, drs. M.W. van, e-mail: `MWETERING@fac.fbk.eur.nl`

Site: Interactive Systems Centre, Magee College,
University of Ulster, Northern Ireland
IP Host: claudia.iscm.ulst.ac.uk
alias: (Ireland) Univ. Ulster 193.63.68.162 s r
Special Note: Please cap transmissions up to 30 Kbps. For further information:

`http://www.iscm.ulst.ac.uk/`
Mike McCool, e-mail: `mike@iscm.ulst.ac.uk`

Site: Weizmann Institute of Science—Computing Center, Rehovot, Israel
IP Host: sunten.weizmann.ac.il
alias: (Israel) Weizmann Inst. 132.76.64.143 s r

Site: Eurocube I.Net, Italy
IP Host: reflector.eurocube.it
alias: (Italy) Eurocube 194.20.44.111 s r
Special Note: Keep the max. bandwidth use up to 30 Kbps. For further information:

`http://www.eurocube.it/video/`
Guido Tripaldi Shamblin, e-mail: `guido@eurocube.it`

Site: Reflector of the Tuscany Metropolitan Area Network, Pisa, Italy
IP Host: indy.iet.unipi.it
alias: (Italy) Univ. Pisa 131.114.9.19 s r

Special Note: It's a Tuscany DQDB fiber-optic network connecting Pisa, Firenze, and Siena. In cooperation with SERRA (SERvizi Rete Ateneo (network university services of Pisa). For further information:

Stefano Giordano, e-mail: `stefano@iet.unipi.it`
Giacomo Guarguaglini, e-mail: `guargua@radar.iet.unipi.it`

Site: Eccosys, Ltd., Tomigaya, Shibuya, Tokyo, Japan
IP Host: neoteny.eccosys.com
alias: (Japan) Eccosys 199.100.7.5 s r
Special Note: For further information:

`http://www.eccosys.com/PEOPLE/JITO/joi.html`
Joichi Ito, e-mail: `jito@eccosys.com`

Site: Future Pirates Broadcast Reflector, Japan
IP Host: bass.fpi.co.jp
alias: (Japan) Future Pirates 202.32.26.17 s r
Special Note: For further information:

`http://www.fpi.jp/Welcome.html`

Site: Department of Applied Molecular Science, Institute for Molecular Science, Okazaki National Research Institutes.
Myodaiji, Okazaki 444, Japan
Japanese Standard Time = GMT + 0900
IP Host: solaris.ims.ac.jp
alias: (Japan) Okazaki NRI 133.48.144.60 s r
Special Note: For further information:

`http://solaris.ims.ac.jp/videoconf.html`
Jiro Toyoda, e-mail: `toyoda@solaris.ims.ac.jp`
94-12-01, toyoda

Site: Research into Artifact Center for Engineering,
University of Tokyo, Tokyo, Japan
IP Host: race-server.race.u-tokyo.ac.jp
alias: (Japan) Univ. Tokyo 157.82.76.2 s r
Special Note: For further information:

`http://www.race.u-tokyo.ac.jp/`
Koji Ando, e-mail: `chutzpah@race.u-tokyo.ac.jp>`
94-10-09, koji-san

Site: Cognitive Science Department, Katholic University of Nijmegen (KUN), The Netherlands (known as Holland to Americans).
IP Host: kunpu7.psych.kun.nl
alias: (Netherlands) Nijmegen Univ. 131.174.200.28 s r
Special Note: Restrain yourself in bandwidth; use talk if possible. For further information:

`http://kunpu7.psych.kun.nl/cogw/nici-cogsci.html`
De Haan, e-mail: `dehaan@nici.kun.nl>`
`http://dehaan1.psych.kun.nl/`
1995-3-13, dehaan

Site: Ostfold Regional College, Informatics Department, Halden, Norway
IP Host: fenris.hiof.no
alias: (Norway) Ostfold/Fenris 158.36.33.3 s r
Special Note: At end of 256 KB line; max bandwidth at 40 Kbps. NASA Select. For further information:

`http://www.ludvigsen.hiof.no/webdoc/video.html`
Barre Ludvigsen, e-mail: `borrel@hiof.no`
Jon Kalnes, e-mail: `jonk@hiof.no`
94-10-29, barre

Site: Norway
IP Host: 158.36.33.5
alias: (Norway) Ostfold/Kark 158.36.33.5 n r
Special Note: Receive only reflector site.

Site: University of Trondheim, Norway, Department of Informatics
IP Host: venus.ifi.unit.no
alias: (Norway) Univ. Trondheim 129.241.161.225 s r
Special Note: Local daytime and evenings. For further information:

`http://www.ifi.unit.no/`
`eyvind.hope@ifi.unit.no`
94-11-27 `eyvind.hope@ifi.unit.no`

Site: University of Lisbon/Faculty of Sciences, Lisbon, Portugal
IP Host: master.di.fc.ul.pt
alias: (Portugal) Univ. Lisbon 192.67.76.40 s r
Special Note: Maintained by the Department of Informatics. For further information:

`http://www.fc.ul.pt`
`cap@di.fc.ul.pt, frazao@di.fc.ul.pt`

Site: National University of Singapore
IP Host: biomed.nus.sg
alias: (Singapore) Univ. Singapore 137.132.9.61 s r
For further information:
K C Lun, e-mail: `coflunkc@leonis.nus.sg`
Tan Tin Wee, e-mail: `bchtantw@leonis.nus.sg`

Site: High-bandwidth "Foeredrag i Lund" broadcast, Lund University Computing Center, Lund, Sweden
IP Host: ForLund-h.video.lu.se
alias: (Sweden) Foeredrag i Lund/Fast 130.235.4.10 s r
Special Note: Broadcast "Foeredrag i Lund" in Swedish at 150 Kbps (120 video + 32 audio) (Compare to ForLund-l.video.lu.se.) For further information:
`http://www.lu.se/ Events`
Jan Engvald, e-mail: `Jan.Engvald@ldc.lu.se`
28 April 1995, Jan

Site: Low-bandwidth "Foeredrag i Lund" broadcast, Lund University Computing Center, Lund, Sweden
IP Host: ForLund-l.video.lu.se
alias: (Sweden) Foeredrag i Lund/Slow 130.235.4.11 s r
Special Note: Broadcast "Foeredrag i Lund" in Swedish at 32 Kbps (Compare to ForLund-h.video.lu.se.) For further information:
`http://www.lu.se/ Events`
Jan Engvald, e-mail: `Jan.Engvald@ldc.lu.se`
28 April 1995, Jan

Site: Lund University Computing Center, Lund, Sweden
IP Host: reflector.lu.se
alias: (Sweden) Lund University 130.235.128.100 s r
Special Note: Videoconferencing with/within Lund University. For further information:
`http://www.lu.se/`
Jan Engvald, e-mail: `Jan.Engvald@ldc.lu.se`
94-11-4, Jan

Site: Lund University Computing Center's NASA Select feed ,
Lund, Sweden
IP Host: reflector.lu.se
alias: (Sweden) NASA Select 130.235.128.100 n r

Special Note: NASA Select. For further information:
`http://www.lu.se/`
Jan Engvald, e-mail: `Jan.Engvald@ldc.lu.se`
94-11-4, Jan

Site: Centre Universitaire d'Informatique Geneva, Switzerland, GMT+1
IP Host: cuisunf.unige.ch
alias: (Switzerland) Geneva Univ. 129.194.12.26 s r
Special Note: Maximum participants: 10. For further information:
`http://cui_www.unige.ch/db-research/Members/mb/mb.html`
Michel Bonjour, e-mail: `bonjour@cui.unige.ch`
95-01-15, Michel

Site: The Open University
IP Host: freud.open.ac.uk
alias: (UK) Open Univ. 137.108.81.14 s r

Site: University of Plymouth, Plymouth, Devon, UK
IP Host: <no DNS entry>
alias: (UK) Plymouth Univ. 141.63.100.8 s r
Special Note: Cap 70 Kbps max. For further information:
`http://tin.ssc.plym.ac.uk/`
Liz Thomson, e-mail: `lt@tin.ssc.plym.ac.uk`
27 April 1995, Liz

Site: Arizona State University, Department of Geology, Tempe, Arizona
IP Host: daffy.la.asu.edu
alias: (USA) ASU Geology Department 129.219.145.149 s r
Special Note: Open to the public. Will periodically be used for private conferences and for Mars Global Surveyor educational outreach programs. For further information:
`http://daisy.la.asu.edu/geopage.html`
Douglas A. Howard, e-mail: `d.howard@asu.edu`
28 April 1995, Douglas

Site: Hallam Trial Reflector Sheffield Hallam University, United Kingdom
IP Host: kingfisher.cms.shu.ac.uk
alias: (UK) Univ. Hallam 143.52.51.15 s r

Special Note: Short-term initially. For further information:

ttp://pine.shu.ac.uk/

Chuck Elliot, e-mail: cmsce@teak.shu.ac.uk

10-26-94, Chuck

Site: Atlanta, Georgia

IP Host: bwigw.bls.com

alias: (USA) Atlanta 192.203.159.8 s r

Special Note: If you'd like a view of 13th and Peachtree Streets. For further information:

Ken Evans, e-mail: evans.ken@wgs-2.bwi.bls.com

28 April 1995

Site: Carnegie Mellon University (CMU), ARPA Speech Group, School of C.S., Pittsburgh, Pennsylvania

IP Host: cutter.speech.cs.cmu.edu

alias: (USA) CMU ARPA Speech 128.2.206.223 s r

Special Note: For further information:

http://www.cs.cmu.edu:8001/Web/SCS-HOME.html

Eric H. Thayer, e-mail: eht+@cs.cmu.edu

94-09-08, eht+

Site: Carnegie Mellon Univ. (CMU), Grad School Industrial Admin.

IP Host: www.gsia.cmu.edu

alias: (USA) CMU GSIA 128.2.230.10 s r

Special Note: Carries NASA Select. For further information:

jds@kudzu.cnidr.org

Site: Clearinghouse for Networked Information Discovery and Retrieval Research, Triangle Park, North Carolina

IP Host: hilda.ncsc.org

alias: (USA) C.N.I.D.R. 128.109.178.103 s r

Special Note: Don't send still screen shots. For further information:

http://kudze.cnidr.org/

Laura M. Craighead, e-mail: lmc@cnidr.org

94-09-08, lmc

Site: Cornell University Public Reflector, Ithaca, New York

IP Host: pro60-test2.cit.cornell.edu

alias: (USA) Cornell Univ. 132.236.91.204 s r

Special Note: >80 Kbps will get you disconnected for ten minutes. Often very busy—please don't stay on long via modem. For further information:

Dick Cogger, e-mail: `r.cogger@cornell.edu`

or

John Lynn, e-mail: `jal7@cornell.edu`

Site: Cream City, Milwaukee, Wisconsin
IP Host: 129.89.70.27
alias: (USA) Cream City 129.89.70.27 s r
Special Note: Always up. For further information:

`http://129.89.70.27:1026/`
Matt Koster, e-mail: `matthewk@csd.uwm.edu`
95-5-1, matthewk

Site: CyberStudios Internet Radio, Ann Arbor, Michigan
IP Host: (No DNS yet)
alias: CyberStudios 141.214.138.248 s r
Special Note: Receive only, 24 hours/day since 4/1/95, Intel DVI 32 Kbps. For further information:

`http://www.umich.edu/~johnlaue/`
John Laue, e-mail: `cyber.studios@umich.edu`
30 Apr 95, John

Site: The Eden Reflector, Austin, Texas
IP Host: matrix.eden.com
alias: (USA) Eden 199.171.21.8 s r
Special Note: Mostly for viewing events. Feel free to use anytime. For further information:

`http://www.eden.com`
`jher@eden.com`
Wed 14 Sep 1994, `jher@eden.com`

Site: Educational Computing Network reflector, Chicago, Illinois
IP Host: uxb1.ecn.bgu.edu
alias: (USA) Educational Comp Netw 143.43.32.61 s r

Site: GTE Laboratories, Inc., Computer & Intelligent Systems Lab, Waltham, Massachusetts
IP Host: albion.gte.com

alias: (USA) GTE-albion 132.197.9.105 s r

Special Note: Please keep bit rates low (30 Kbps or less). For further information:

John Nicol, e-mail: `nicol@gte.com`,
fax: 617.466.4229, 617.466.2060

Site: GTE Laboratories, Inc., Advanced Local Area Network Testbed, Waltham, Massachusetts

IP Host: skyhawk.gte.com

alias: (USA) GTE-skyhawk 132.197.70.1 s r

Special Note: Please keep bit rates low (40 Kbps or less); soon to operate on a Fast Ethernet and ATM network. For further information:

`http://www-lanlab.gte.com/`
Alan Bugos, e-mail: `abugos@gte.com`, 617.466.2698
94-12-05, abugos

Site: International Institute of Theoretical and Applied Physics, Ames, Iowa

IP Host: pv70f2.vincent.iastate.edu

alias: (USA) IITAP NASA Select 129.186.112.242 s r

Special Note: NASA Select reflector (Don't send video if only watching). For further information:

`http://www.physics.iastate.edu/`
Douglas Fils, e-mail: `fils@iastate.edu`
4-19-95, fils

Site: International Institute of Theoretical and Applied Physics, Ames, Iowa

IP Host: pv746d.vincent.iastate.edu

alias: (USA) IITAP129.186.116.109 s r

Special Note: General reflector. For further information:

`http://www.physics.iastate.edu/`
Douglas Fils, e-mail: `fils@iastate.edu`
4-19-95, fils

Site: Intelecom Data Systems (IDS) World Network Public Reflector, East Greenwich, Rhode Island

IP Host: reflector.ids.net

alias: (USA) Intelecom Data Systems 155.212.1.12 s r

Special Note: Standard bandwidth restrictions apply for inbound users; IDS customers and IDS InterCable Net customers can boost it up as high as they want. For further information:

> http://www.ids.net/
> Andy Green, e-mail: green@ids.net
> 950103, Andy Green, e-mail: green@ids.net

Site: Indiana State University, Terre Haute, Indiana, USA
IP Host: mama.indstate.edu
alias: (USA) Indiana State Univ. 139.102.70.201 s r
Special Note: Attempts to maintain a 24-hour-a-day signal on a greenhouse! For further information:

> Timothy Mulkey, e-mail: lsmulky@scifac.indstate.edu

Site: Kent State University's NASA Select relay, Kent, Ohio
IP Host: axon.kent.edu
alias: (USA) Kent State NASA Select 131.123.5.1 s r
Special Note: NASA Select relay. For further information:

> http://netgopher.lerc.nasa.gov/NASA_Select/NASA_Select.html
> Greg Madey, e-mail: gmadey@synapse.kent.edu
> 25 April 1995, Greg

Site: Kent State University College of Business Administration, Kent, Ohio
IP Host: business.kent.edu
alias: (USA) Kent State Univ. 131.123.5.2 s r
Special Note: For further information:

> http://business.kent.edu/
> Greg Madey, e-mail: gmadey@synapse.kent.edu
> 25 April 1995, Greg

Site: KJHK 90.7 FM, Kansas
IP Host: 129.237.117.95
alias: (USA) KJHK radio 129.237.117.95 s r
Special Note: For further information

> http://www.cc.ukans.edu/~burcham/index.html
> Rob Burcham, e-mail: burchamr@falcon.cc.ukans.edu

Site: KUGS-FM 89.3, Bellingham, Washington
IP Host: olympic.pacificrim.net

alias: (USA) KUGS-FM 204.96.68.1 s r

Special Note: College nonprofit station specializing in college alternative rock. For further information:

`http://pacificrim.net/~kugs/`

Gavin Shearer, Promotions Director, e-mail: `gavin@pacificrim.net`

27 Aug 95, Gavin

Site: LappDoggware Co.

IP Host: laird.ccds.cincinnati.oh.us

alias: (USA) LappDoggware 129.137.180.2 s r

Special Note: For further information:

John Lee, e-mail: `leejb@laird.ccds.cincinnati.oh.us`

Site: laUNChpad, Extended Bulletin Board Service, University of North Carolina, Chapel Hill, North Carolina

IP Host: lambada.oit.unc.edu

alias: (USA) laUNChpad EBBS 152.2.22.80 s r

Special Note: E-mail, USENet, gopher, and other research services (free, public access to the world-at-large). For further information:

Williams, Michael G., e-mail: `michael@lambada.oit.unc.edu`

Site: University Libraries Systems Dept, King Library, Miami University, Oxford, Ohio

IP Host: old-holmes.lib.muohio.edu

alias: (USA) Miami Univ. (Ohio) 134.53.24.5 s r

Special Note: For further information:

Peter Murray, e-mail: `MurrayPE@muohio.edu`

25 Oct 1994, Peter

Site: NASA Select Reflector, Lewis Research, Cleveland, Ohio

IP Host: quark.lerc.nasa.gov

alias: (USA) NASA Select 139.88.27.43 n r

Special Note: Receive only, please. For further information:

`http://netgopher.lerc.nasa.gov/NASA_Select/NASA_Select.html`

Michael Baldizzi, e-mail: `mbaldizzi@lerc.nasa.gov`, +1.216.433.5120

94-09-08, mbaldizzi

Site: Network Solutions, Inc., Herndon, Virginia

IP Host: nic.ops.netsol.com

alias: (USA) Network Solutions 198.41.0.200 s r

Special Note: This is a public reflector restricting clients to 80 Kbps. Currently configured for MAVEN/VAT; NV- and multicast-capable. For further information:

`http://www.netsol.com/`

`stanb@netsol.com`

Site: North Carolina State University Multimedia Lab, Raleigh, North Carolina
IP Host: magneto.csc.ncsu.edu
alias: (USA) N. Carolina State Univ. 152.1.57.56 s r
Special Note: For further information:

`http://magneto.csc.ncsu.edu/`

Scott Callicutt, e-mail: `sfcallic@magneto.csc.ncsu.edu`

Site: NYSERNet (New York State Education and Research Network), Liverpool, New York
IP Host: nysernet.org
alias: (USA) NYSERNet 192.77.173.2 s r
Special Note: Please don't send still shots to this reflector. For further information:

`http://nysernet.org/`

Jean Armour Polly, e-mail: `jpolly@nysernet.org, don@nysernet.org`

94-09-08, jpolly

Site: Academic Technology Services, The Ohio State University, Columbus, Ohio
IP Host: davros.acs.ohio-state.edu
alias: (USA) Ohio State Univ. 128.146.116.8 n r
Special Note: Don't send still screen shots. For further information:

`http://www.acs.ohio-state.edu/`

Harpal Chohan, e-mail: `chohan+@osu.edu`

94-11-18, hsc

Site: Center for Academic Computing, Penn. State, University Park, Pennsylvania
IP Host: hornet.cac.psu.edu
alias: (USA) Penn State 128.118.58.54 s r
Special Note: CU-SeeMe users should still keep their settings down. For further information:

`http://www.psu.edu/`

John Kalbach, e-mail: `kalbach@cac.psu.edu`

94-09-08, rod_murchison

Site: Archer Instructional Media Center, Seattle Pacific University, Seattle, Washington
IP Host: adam.spu.edu

alias: (USA) Seattle Pacific Univ. 192.190.33.9 s r
Special Note: Typically on from 8 a.m.–5 p.m. Pacific Time, Monday–Friday. For further information:

Tim Kennedy, e-mail: `tkennedy@spu.edu`
94-12-01, Tim

Site: Sprintlink (Sprint Telecommunications Corp.), Herndon, Virginia
IP Host: tiny.sprintlink.net
alias: (USA) Sprintlink 199.0.55.90 s r
Special Note: For further information:

`http://www.sprintlink.net`
Richard Martin, e-mail: `rmartin@stealth.sprintlink.net`

Site: Stanford University Medical Center, Stanford, California
IP Host: mednet2.stanford.edu
alias: (USA) Stanford Univ. Med Ctr 171.65.4.4 s r
Special Note: For further information:

`http://www-med.stanford.edu/MedCenter/reflect.html`
John Reuling, e-mail: `reuling@med.stanford.edu`
95-02-18, reuling

Site: ThePoint Internet Services, Kentucky
IP Host: cuseeme.thepoint.net
alias: (USA) ThePoint 198.6.9.2 s r
Special Note: For further information:

`http://www.thepoint.net/`
Michael Jung, e-mail: `mikej@thepoint.net`

Site: University of Hawaii, Digital Media Lab, Hawaii
IP Host: makaha.mic.hawaii.edu
alias: (USA) Univ. Hawaii 128.171.171.10 s r
Special Note: For further information:

`http://www.mic.hawaii.edu`
Craig, e-mail: `webmaster@www.mic.hawaii.edu`

Site: University of Kansas, Special Education Video Conferencing Site, Kansas
IP Host: chef.sped.ukans.edu
alias: (USA) Univ. Kansas 129.237.247.160 s r

Site: Administrative Information Systems,
Alumni Hall, University of Maine, Orono, Maine
IP Host: <no DNS entry>
alias: (USA) Univ. Maine 130.111.120.13 s r
Special Note: For further information:
`http://www.umeais.maine.edu/`
`wheeler@cardinal.umeais.maine.edu`

Site: University of Maryland, College Park, Maryland
IP Host: haven.umd.edu
alias: (USA) Univ. Maryland 128.8.10.6 s r
Special Note: Experimental site. For further information:
`http://www.ni.umd.edu/`
Dan Magorian, e-mail: `magorian@ni.umd.edu`
28 Apr 95, Dan

Site: University of Michigan Medical Center, Michigan
IP Host: cliff.itn.med.umich.edu
alias: (USA) Univ. Michigan 141.214.252.170 s r
Special Note: Audio capable; Mike's personal Sparc SLC. For further information:
mike, e-mail: `squids@umich.edu`
22 Jan 1995, mike, e-mail: `squids@umich.edu`

Site: University of Pennsylvania Office of Data Comm. and Computing Services,
Philadelphia, Pennsylvania
IP Host: isis.dccs.upenn.edu
alias: (USA) Univ. Penn 130.91.72.36 s r
Special Note: Short times and minimal audio, please. For further information
`http://www.upenn.edu/`
`danu@dccs.upenn.edu`

Site: University of Texas, Austin, Texas
IP Host: doc.cc.utexas.edu
alias: (USA) Univ. Texas 128.83.108.14 s r
Special Note: Fairly stable. Currently linked with qms.com. For further information:
`http://ccwf.cc.utexas.edu/~streak/`
Jason Williams, e-mail: `streak@ccwf.cc.utexas.edu`

Site: Virginia Commonwealth University, Richmond, Virginia
IP Host: cabell.vcu.edu
alias: (USA) VA Commonwealth Univ. 128.172.157.244 s r
Special Note: For further information:

Jeff Price, e-mail: `jprice@cabell.vcu.edu`
94-12-94, jeff

appendix

MBone Keywords and Acronyms

The following is an example of the acronyms commonly associated with the MBone. This should be a helpful reference for you during the course of reading this book.

Acronym	Full Name
ACM	Association for Computing Machinery
ADPCM	Adaptive Differential Pulse Code Modulation
ASCII	American Standard Code for Information Exchange
ATM	Asynchronous Transfer Mode
CCD	Charged Coupled Device
CCITT	Comité Consultatif International de Télégraphique et Téléphonique (also known as ITU)
CODEC	Coder/Decoder
CUSM	Cornell University CU-SeeMe
DVMRP	Distance Vector Multicast Routing Protocol
FDDI	Fiber Distributed Data Interface
FTP	File Transfer Protocol
GIF	Graphical Interchange Format
GSM	Group Speciale Mobile
HTTP	HyperText Transport Protocol
IAB	Internet Advisory Board
ICMP	Internet Control Message Protocol
IDVI	Intel Digital Video Interactive
IEEE	Institute of Electrical and Electronics Engineers
IETF	Internet Engineering Task Force
IGMP	Internet Group Management Protocol
IP	Internet Protocol
IPv4	Current version of IP (4)
ISDN	Integrated Services Digital Network
ITU	International Telecommunication Union
IVS	INRIA Videoconferencing System
JPEG	Joint Photographic Experts Group

Acronym	Full Name
Kbps	Kilobits per second
LAN	Local Area Network
LPC	Linear Predictive Coding
MBone	Multicast Backbone on the Internet
Mbps	Megabits per second
MIME	Multipurpose Internet Mail Extensions
MOSPF	Multicast Open Shortest Path First
MPEG	Motion Picture Experts Group
MROUTED	Multicast Routing Daemon
Nevot	Network Voice Terminal
NSFNet	National Science Foundation Network
NTSC	National Television Standards Committee
NV	NetVideo
OSI	Open Systems Interconnection
OSPF	Open Shortest Path First
PAL	Phase Alternation Line
PCM	Pulse Code Modulation
PIM	Protocol Independent Multicasting
PS	PostScript format
RFC	Request For Comments
RIP	Router Information Protocol
RSVP	Resource Reservation Protocol
RTP	Real-Time Protocol
SD	Session Directory
SECAM	Sequential Couleur A Memoire
TCP/IP	Transmission Control Protocol/Internet Protocol

continues

Acronym	Full Name
TTL	Time To Live
UDP	User Datagram Protocol
VAT	Visual Audio Tool
WAN	Wide Area Network
WB	WhiteBoard
WWW	World Wide Web

part

Bibliography

bibliography

This bibliography lists, by chapter, the sources utilized and references cited by the author throughout this book. A number has been assigned to each source accordingly, and this particular number is the key reference used when citing a source within each chapter.

Chapter 1

[1] Tenenbaum, A.S., *Computer Networks, Second Edition*, Englewood Cliffs, NJ: Prentice Hall, 1989.

[2] Stevens, W.R., *Unix Network Programming*, Englewood Cliffs, NJ: Prentice Hall, 1990.

[3] Partridge, C., "Fixing the Internet Protocol," *IEEE Network* (July 1993): 4–5.

[4] Schulzrinne, H., "Voice Communication Across the Internet: A Network Voice Terminal," *Technical Report* (1992).

[5] DeTreville, J. and D.W. Sincoskie, "A Distributed Experimental Communications System," *IEEE Journal on Selected Areas in Communications* SAC-1 (Dec. 1983): 1070–1075.

[6] Deering, S., "Host Extensions for IP Multicasting," Network Working Group Request for Comments, RFC 1112, Stanford University, 1989.

[7] Comer, D.E., *Internetworking with TCP/IP, Vol. 1*, Englewood Cliffs, NJ: Prentice Hall, 1991.

[8] Rodriguez, A.A. and L.A. Rowe, "Multimedia Systems and Applications," *IEEE Computer Magazine* (May 1995): 20–22.

[9] Forgie, F.W., "Voice Conferencing in Packet Networks," International Conference on Communications, IEEE, Seattle, WA (June 1980): 21.3.1–21.3.4.

[10] Cohen, D., "Specification for the Network Voice Protocol NVP," Network Working Group Request for Comments, RFC 741, ISI, January 1976.

[11] Cole, R., "Pvp—A Packet Video Protocol," W-Note 28, ISI, University of Southern California, Los Angeles, CA, August 1981.

[12] Macedonia, M.R. and D.P. Brutzman, "MBone Provides Audio and Video Across the Internet," *IEEE Computer Magazine* (April 1994): 30–36.

[13] Casner, S. and S. Deering, "First IETF Internet Audiocast," *ACM SIGComm Computer Communications Review* (July 1992): 92–97.

[14] Waitzman, D., C. Partridge, and S. Deering, "Distance Vector Multicasting Routing Protocol," Network Working Group Request for Comments, Internet RFC-1075, November 1988.

[15] Moy, John, "Multicast Routing Extensions for OSPF," *Communications of the ACM* 37 (August 1994): 61–66.

[16] Lewis, P., "Peering Out a Real Time Window," *New York Times*, Wednesday, 8 February 1995.

[17] Bank, D., "Agent of Change," *San Jose Mercury Newspaper*, Sunday, 8 January 1995, pp. 1E, 4E.

[18] Weiss, A., "Stretching the MBone: The Internet Broadcasting Network," *Internet World Magazine* (March 1995): 38–41.

Chapter 2

[1] Furht, B., D. Kalra, F.L. Kitson, et.al., "Design Issues for Interactive Television Systems," *IEEE Computer Magazine* (May 1995): 25–39.

[2] Berners-Lee, T.J., R. Cailliau, J.F. Groff, and B. Pollermann, CERN, "World-Wide Web: The Information Universe," *Electronic Networking: Research, Applications, and Policy* 2, no 1 (Spring, 1992): 52–58, Westport, CT: Meckler Publishing.

[3] Krol, Ed, *The Whole Internet User's Guide and Catalog*, Sebastopol, CA: O'Reilly Associates, 1992. (ISBN 1-56592-025-2)

[4] Berners-Lee, T.J., "Uniform Resource Locators (URLs)," Internet Draft, URI Working Group, March 1994.

[5] Tang, John, "", Sun Microsystems.

[6] Harrison, S. and S. Minneman, "The Use of Video as Design Medium," *Fourth Annual Symposium on Concurrent Engineering* (June 1992): 93–106.

[7] Kumar, V., J. Glicksman, and G. Kramer, "A SHAREd Web to Support Design Teams," IEEE Workshop on Enabling Technologies, Morgantown, WV, April 1994.

[8] Macedonia, M.R. and D.P. Brutzman, "MBone Provides Audio and Video Across The Internet," *IEEE Computer Magazine* (April 1994): 30–36.

[9] P. Venkat Rangan, H.M. Vin, and S. Ramanathan, "Designing an On-Demand Multimedia Service," *IEEE Communications Magazine* 30, no. 7 (July 1992).

[10] Braden, R., D. Clark, and S. Shenker, "Integrated Services in the Internet Architecture: an Overview," Internet RFC-1633, June 1994.

[11] Braden, R., D. Estrin, S. Herzog, and S. Jamin, "Resource Reservation Protocol (RSVP): Version 1 Functional Specification," Internet Draft, May 16, 1995

[12] Schulzrinne, H., S. Casner, R. Frederick, and V. Jacobson, "RTP: A Transport Protocol for Real-Time Applications," Internet Draft, IETF-AVT WG, March, 1995.

Chapter 3

[1] Stevens, Richard W., *TCP/IP Illustrated Volume 1: The Protocols*, Addison-Wesley Publishing, 1994.

[2] Comer, Doug, *Internetworking with TCP/IP*.

[3] ACM Communications, Moy, John, "Multicast Routing Extensions for OSPF," *Communications of the ACM* 37 (August 1994): 61–66.

[4] ACM Communications, Eriksson, Hans, "MBone: The Multicast Backbone," *Communications of the ACM* 37 (August 1994): 54–60.

[5] IEEE Computer, Macedonia, M.R. and D.P. Brutzman, "MBone Provides Audio and Video Across the Internet," *IEEE Computer* 27 no. 4 (April 1994): 30–36.

[6] INET'93, Eriksson, Hans, "MBone—The Multicast Backbone," INET 1993.

[7] ACM SIGCOMM, Casner, S. and S. Deering, "First IETF Internet Audiocast," *ACM SIGCOMM Computer Communications Review*, San Diego, CA (July 1992): 92–97.

[8] Deering, S., "Host Extensions for IP Multicasting," Network Working Group Request for Comments, Internet RFC-1112, August 1989.

[9] Waitzman, D., C. Partridge, and S. Deering, "Distance Vector Multicasting Routing Protocol," Network Working Group Request for Comments, Internet RFC-1075, November 1988.

[10] Schulzrinne, H., S. Casner, R. Frederick, and V. Jacobson, "RTP: A Transport Protocol for Real-Time Applications," July 18, 1994.

[11] Ballardine, T. and B. Fenner, "Inter-Domain Multicast Routing (IDMR)."

[12] Casner, S. and S. Deering, "First IETF Internet Audiocast," *ConneXions* no. 6 (June 1992): 10–17.

[13] Deering, S., D. Estrin, D. Farinacci, V. Jacobson, C. Liu, and L. Wei, "Protocol Independent Multicast PIM: Specification," Working Internet Draft, November 1994.

[14] Deering, S. and D. Cheriton, "Multicast Routing in Datagram Internetworks and Extended LANs," *ACM Transactions on Computer Systems* (May 1990): 85–111.

Chapter 4

[1] Floyd, S., V. Jacobson, and S. McCanne, "A Reliable Multicast Framework for Light-Weight Sessions and Application Level Framing," ACM SIGCOMM 1995.

Chapter 5

[1] Banerjee, A., E.W. Knightly, F.L. Templin, and H. Zhang, "Experiments with the Tenet Real-Time Protocol Suite on the Sequoia 2000 Wide Area Network," *Second ACM Multimedia Conference Proceedings*, San Francisco, CA (October 1994): 183–191.

[2] Stonebraker, M., "An Overview of the Sequoia 2000 Project," *Proceedings of COMPCON '92*, San Francisco, CA (February 1992).

[3] Weiser, M. and A. Garman, "Bleeding Edge Technology—From Coats to Market Caps," *The Red Herring* (August 1995): 58.

[4] Partridge, C., "Gigabit Networking," Addison-Wesley Publishing, 1993. (ISBN 0-201-56333-9)

Chapter 6

[1] Siyan, K. and C. Hare, *Internet Firewalls and Network Security*, New Riders Publishing, 1995. (ISBN 1-56205-437-6)

2] Cheswick, W.R. and S. M. Bellovin, *Firewalls and Internet Security: Repelling the Wily Hacker*, Addison-Wesley Publishing, 1994. (ISBN 0-201-63357-4)

index

Symbols

A

B

C

D

E

F

G

H

I

J

K

L

M

N

O

P

Q-R

S

T

U

V

W–Z

PLUG YOURSELF INTO...

THE MACMILLAN INFORMATION SUPERLIBRARY™

Free information and vast computer resources from the world's leading computer book publisher—online!

FIND THE BOOKS THAT ARE RIGHT FOR YOU!
A complete online catalog, plus sample chapters and tables of contents give you an in-depth look at *all* of our books, including hard-to-find titles. It's the best way to find the books you need!

- STAY INFORMED with the latest computer industry news through our online newsletter, press releases, and customized Information SuperLibrary Reports.
- GET FAST ANSWERS to your questions about MCP books and software.
- VISIT our online bookstore for the latest information and editions!
- COMMUNICATE with our expert authors through e-mail and conferences.
- DOWNLOAD SOFTWARE from the immense MCP library:
  - Source code and files from MCP books
  - The best shareware, freeware, and demos
- DISCOVER HOT SPOTS on other parts of the Internet.
- WIN BOOKS in ongoing contests and giveaways!

TO PLUG INTO MCP:

WORLD WIDE WEB: **http://www.mcp.com**

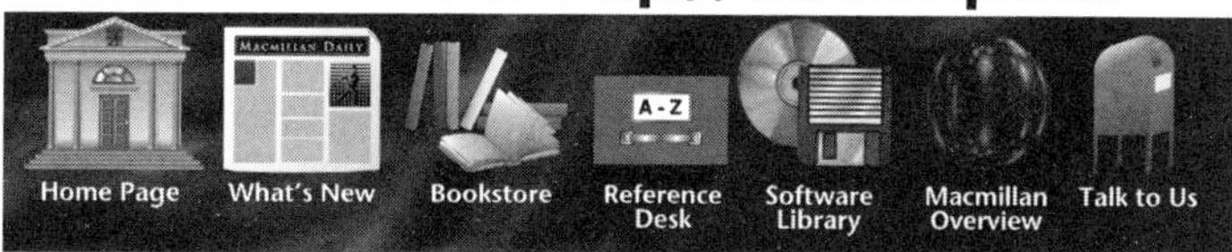

GOPHER: gopher.mcp.com

FTP: ftp.mcp.com